Given the pressing time constraints  agement tends to be overlooked and and/or unnecessary exercise ... Yet life that the best way to delay a pr ignoring essential delivery processe. This book is definitely a must-read for anyone with keen interest in g PM practices.

– Kana Mutombo (PhD Maritime),
Principal Engineer at Transnet National Ports Authority

Whether you are a novice, a seasoned project manager, or even a student, I have no doubt that the content covered here will meet your needs for any project in dealing with the often volatile stakeholder management dynamics ... With my 15+ years of mentoring project managers in Central and Southern Africa, I highly recommend this publication.

– Peter Banda (PhD Fellow/NUST, MSc, APM),
CEO of Project Management Zimbabwe

How to Manage Project Stakeholders

This book outlines how to identify stakeholders, analyse their stakes, and plan and implement an engagement strategy to secure relevant input and dependable buy-in to assure the successful delivery of Large Infrastructure Projects. It also addresses common stakeholder management "inadequacies" and is supplemented with four extended practical exercises to help readers apply the principles to their own large, complex projects and ensure project success.

The project management industry, particularly the Large Infrastructure Projects domain, has only recently awakened to the reality that failed Stakeholder Management probably leads to a failure of the project altogether. Due to the complexities involved, most traditional approaches to managing stakeholders have developed serious difficulties in dealing with large and complex projects. This book presents a Systems Thinking approach to managing stakeholders that accommodates these complexities and seeks to crystallise the notion that "managing projects means managing stakeholders", while also introducing an ethical perspective (i.e., stakeholders have legitimate rights regardless of their power to influence the project). This shifts the paradigm from "Management of Stakeholders" to "Management for Stakeholders".

It is essential reading for all those involved with managing large projects including project managers, sponsors, and executives. It will also be useful for advanced students of project management and systems engineering looking to understand and expand their knowledge of infrastructure projects and Systems Engineering.

Pascal Bohulu Mabelo has more than 20 years of professional experience and possesses a wide range of technical and managerial skills pertaining to projects. He has previously served as the national chairman of Project Management South Africa (PMSA) and is a regular speaker at project management conferences and seminars. He promotes the application of Systems Engineering concepts to unravel complexity in Large Infrastructure Projects.

How to Manage Project Stakeholders

Effective Strategies for Successful Large Infrastructure Projects

Pascal Bohulu Mabelo

Routledge
Taylor & Francis Group

LONDON AND NEW YORK

First published 2020 by Routledge

2 Park Square, Milton Park, Abingdon, Oxon OX14 4RN
605 Third Avenue, New York, NY 10017

Routledge is an imprint of the Taylor & Francis Group, an informa business

First issued in paperback 2022

Publisher's Note

The publisher has gone to great lengths to ensure the quality of this reprint
but points out that some imperfections in the original copies may be apparent.

British Library Cataloguing-in-Publication Data
A catalogue record for this book is available from the British Library

Library of Congress Cataloging-in-Publication Data
Names: Bohulu Mabelo, Pascal, 1969–author.
Title: How to manage project stakeholders: effective strategies for
successful large infrastructure projects/Pascal Bohulu Mabelo.
Description: 1 Edition. | New York: Routledge, 2020. |
Includes bibliographical references and index.
Identifiers: LCCN 2019056469 (print) | LCCN 2019056470 (ebook) |
ISBN 9780367903305 (hardback) | ISBN 9781003023791 (ebook)
Subjects: LCSH: Business planning. | Industrial management. |
Infrastructure (Economics)
Classification: LCC HD30.28 .B647 2020 (print) |
LCC HD30.28 (ebook) |
DDC 658.4/04–dc23
LC record available at https://lccn.loc.gov/2019056469
LC ebook record available at https://lccn.loc.gov/2019056470

ISBN: 978-0-367-90330-5 (hbk)
ISBN: 978-1-03-233647-3 (pbk)
DOI: 10.4324/9781003023791

Typeset in Bembo
by Deanta Global Publishing Services, Chennai, India

To my God-given wife and children,

To the project management fraternity across Africa and the Diaspora,

I humbly dedicate this work.

Contents

Figures

Tables

About the author

Pascal Bohulu Mabelo MBA, MSc (Eng), Pr Eng (South Africa), Pr CPM (South Africa), PMP

Pascal possesses a wide range of technical and managerial skills pertaining to infrastructure projects and has had the opportunity to work in an array of large-scale projects with people from various backgrounds. He presently works as a principal consultant through his own practice, E 6 Project Consulting (Pty) Ltd, and contracts on diverse assignments in both the private and public sector.

Pascal has worked in large projects as a design engineer, project/programme manager, project consultant, and project management executive; he had previously established, and for eight years headed up, the Project Management Centre of Excellence at the "capital projects" division of a multi-billion Rand company in South Africa. Having earned more than 20 years of professional experience in the industry, he has steadily built up an extensive network of relationships in the industry and was honoured to serve as the national chairman of PM South Africa (PMSA), the leading project management professional association in Southern Africa.

Pascal is also well known in the industry for having authored several articles in project management magazines and journals, and has guest lectured on project-related processes at various top-ranked South African universities, not to mention speaking at project management conferences and seminars. He is currently promoting the application of Systems Thinking and/or Systems Engineering principles and concepts to unravel complexity in Large Infrastructure Projects (LIPs) in order to address their persistent risks of failure – and their massive, pernicious cost and schedule overruns.

About this book

The project management industry, the Large Infrastructure Projects sector in particular, has only recently awakened to the reality that failed Stakeholder Management probably leads to a failure of the project altogether. For at the time the author published the article, "Managing Project Stakeholders" (in the July and September 2009 editions of *ProjectNet* Journal of PM South Africa), PMBoK still reflected this practice as a branch of Communications Management; that only changed at the advent of the fifth edition (2013). PMBoK argued in 2013:

> Information on stakeholder identification and managing stakeholder expectations was moved from ... Project Communications Management to this new Knowledge Area to expand upon and increase the focus on the importance of appropriately engaging project stakeholders in the key decisions ... associated with the project.

Nonetheless, infrastructure projects are becoming increasingly larger and more complex. Their impact on various stakeholders is expanding even more, which as a result not only attracts a broader "audience" of stakeholders, but also makes their actions or attitudes vis-à-vis the project extremely pertinent in terms of assuring project success. Therefore, Stakeholder Management should be done properly to avoid complications in such projects.

Due to the complexities involved, most traditional approaches to managing stakeholders have developed serious difficulties in dealing with large and complex projects. For that reason, the author has *reloaded* and expanded upon the 2009 instalments to present a Systems Thinking approach to managing stakeholders that accommodates complexities.

One other "inadequacy" plaguing Stakeholder Management was in the failure of many traditional approaches to discuss and elucidate the exact purpose(s) of this process.

While identifying and analysing stakeholders is crucial, understanding that the whole process is aimed at (1) securing relevant input and (2) securing dependable buy-in on the part of relevant stakeholders across the Systems-of-Interest is equally important. Hence, this book also makes a deliberate attempt to address this peculiar inadequacy.

Furthermore, this volume seeks to crystallise the notion that "managing projects means managing stakeholders", while also introducing an ethical perspective (i.e., stakeholders have legitimate rights regardless of their power to influence the project). This shifts the paradigm from "Management *of* Stakeholders" to "Management *for* Stakeholders" – basically moving away from "spending management attention and resources on a few stakeholders due to their high harm/help potential" to "trying to create win-win situations for all stakeholders", while still abiding by a set of priorities in line with project objectives.

Foreword

The author's desire to share his experiential knowledge and academic thinking led to his first book, "Successful System Deployment through Operational Readiness". The book received a very favourable review in the *PM World Journal* (Vol. VIII, Issue VIII – September 2019) written by Ivan Kotcher (PMP) who expressed that

> This book is a welcome addition to the art of thinking holistically about why even well-executed projects can result in outcomes that do not succeed in helping the business or governmental organization executing them, and addressing what critical success factors are involved in guiding positive integration with the preexisting environment.

The author's passion and humility, when speaking about his experience in project management and involvement in infrastructure projects, is infectious and inspiring. Once again, in this follow-up book, he demonstrates his application of the "art of thinking holistically" about Stakeholder Management, another topical and often under-emphasised aspect within the realm of management of Large Infrastructure Projects.

It is pointed out in this book that while Stakeholder Management forms part of the body of knowledge for project management, it is often overlooked as a vital part of the process in managing Large Infrastructure Projects. Placing the engagement of stakeholders "on the periphery" of the project leads to the derailment of the project. To avoid issues arising from stakeholders, these people, organisations, and political entities, internal and external to the project, need to be identified in the early phases of the project and duly included in the decision-making process. This becomes increasingly important as projects become larger and more complex, and the number and variety of stakeholders increase proportionately, as is the case in Large Infrastructure Projects.

This book provides a roadmap for practitioners and academics on how to effectively identify, engage, manage, and communicate with and build buy-in from key project stakeholders in order to avoid, as far as possible, unforeseen disruptions arising from disenfranchised stakeholders. Keep this book close at hand when you start a project or else find yourself facing disgruntled stakeholders at some point in implementation; apply the principles discoursed herein and you will succeed in any business endeavour!

Bernadette P. Sunjka, Pr Eng, PMP[1]

---

1   Bernadette P. Sunjka is a senior lecturer and head of stream in Industrial Engineering at the University of Witwatersrand; she worked as a senior project manager in banking and at Eskom.

Acronyms

E6PC	E 6 Project consulting (Pty) Ltd, consultancy in South Africa
EIA	Environmental Impact Assessment
Eskom	State-owned power utility company of South Africa
ICT	Information and Communications Technology
INCOSE	International Council on Systems Engineering
KPMG	Global accounting and consultancy firm
NETLIPSE	Network for the dissemination of knowledge on the management and organisation of Large Infrastructure Projects in Europe
NPV	Net Present Value
PM	Project Management
PMBoK	Project Management Body of Knowledge
PMI	Project Management Institute (i.e., custodian of the PMBoK)
PMP	Project Management Professional (i.e., registered with PMI)
RACI	Responsible-Accountable-Consulted-Informed
SADC	Southern Africa Development Community
SAICA	South African Institute of Chartered Accountants

1 Introduction

Stakeholder Management (SM) is fast becoming a "knowledge area" of focus in Project Management (PM); entire sections are dedicated to this topic in the recent literature. There is a growing realisation that any inadequate or sheer omission of Stakeholder Management is an open invitation for complications and to failure in large projects.

Yet a Large Infrastructure Projects survey in 2015[35] revealed that 23% of entities do not consider SM as a "core" project activity; in half of those entities, respondents could not even tell whether SM was core or not – this just shows how confused many entities might be about SM in their megaprojects. Many project practitioners still treat SM as an "off-line" and/or "ad hoc" process; in truth, some found it somewhat degrading, an embarrassment that they should be expected to manage stakeholders!

When referring to a stakeholder, one shall appreciate that the operative word is stake. A "stake" is the degree to which one is involved in something ... or wants it to succeed or fail. So virtually every entity (e.g., organisations, individuals) "interacting" in the project environment constitutes a "project stakeholder", and is important in projects, be they infrastructure (e.g., power plant, rail/road network, hospital) or information and communications technology (ICT) in nature (Figure 1.1).

Since 2013, PMBoK[47] has included Stakeholder Management as a "specific Knowledge Area"; "The Knowledge Areas are: Project Integration Management, Project Scope Management, Project Time Management ... and Project Stakeholder Management. Each Knowledge Area within the PMBoK® Guide is contained in a separate section". PMBoK further states:

> Stakeholders are persons or organisations (e.g., customers, sponsors, the performing organisation, or the public), [i]who are actively involved in the project or [ii]whose interest may be positively and negatively affected by the performance or the completion [or outcomes]

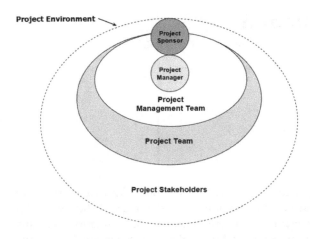

Figure 1.1 Relationship between stakeholders and the project, as per Ambler[4]

of the project. Stakeholders may also exert influence over the project, its deliverables, and the project team members.[47]

Both are involved!

From this definition, it is clear stakeholders are not "bystanders, those folks out there", but include "those who are actively involved ... or affected" – e.g., community or project team. Moreover, Freeman proceeded to suggest, "A stakeholder in an organisation [e.g., project] is (by definition) any group or individual who can affect or is [or could be] affected by the achievement of the organisation's [e.g., project's] objectives".[21]

The notion of stakeholder is *inextricably* linked to objectives; for stakes derive from the pursuit of objectives. Hence:

> The most important issue in project management is for the project manager to get project staff, beneficiaries, and other stakeholders to develop a common understanding, agreement, and commitment to a project's objectives. A shared perception about objectives, agreement that the project is worth doing [i.e. stakes], and the commitment to make it happen does not happen automatically. It takes effort and involves a considerable amount of communication [i.e. engagements].[72]

In fact, in a video material titled, "Accepting Accountability When Things Go Wrong", Morris (PMP)[42] suggests the main reasons for project breakdown include the following: (1) insufficient or disorganised communication; (2) lack of continuous risk identification and mitigation management; (3) inconsistent issue management resulting in delayed resolutions; and (4) inadequate vendor or stakeholder engagement management. Items (1) and (4) *directly* relate to SM, while items (2) and (3) still *partially* relate to SM.

Morris further contends, "These are key areas that must be managed well for project success; the slightest breakdown in any of those areas will cause a negative ripple throughout the project".[42] It therefore follows that "the slightest breakdown in Stakeholder Management will cause a negative ripple throughout the project", even leading to failure. Indeed, inadequate or failed Stakeholder Management would lead to project failure, particularly (it shall again be underscored) in large and complex projects!

INCOSE[25] maintains, "There is a near unanimous agreement that successful projects depend on meeting the needs and requirements of the stakeholder/customer". Hence, "You increase the likelihood of customer acceptance and delight at the end of your project if you manage stakeholder expectations from concept through delivery".[7] Accordingly, the project manager "works through the issues raised and facilitates resolutions in order to avoid discouraging or disengaging stakeholders [i.e. in LIPs]".[46]

Therefore, Stakeholder Management should not be a mere public relations exercise; SM has a twofold, intertwined purpose. SM purposes align to the notion of Corporate Social Responsibility (CSR). The World Business Council for Sustainable Development[55] states that CSR is, "The continuing commitment by business to behave ethically and contribute to economic development while improving [not ruin] the quality of life of the workforce and their families as well as of the local community and society at large".

It is accordingly expected that business should apply the same "principle" in all their projects and/or similar endeavours, and should thus consider the needs, concerns, or interests of various stakeholders in the project environment. By way of confirmation, a recent survey conducted by KPMG and the United Nations Environmental Programme has also revealed that stakeholders are generally concerned with the following issues:

(1) The quality of the company's product or service [i.e., input to requirements];
(2) The trust and confidence [i.e., buy-in] the stakeholders have in the company.

A summary of the King III Report on Governance for South Africa also noted "It is evident that stakeholders [i.e. their input and buy-in] cannot be ignored". Moreover, in "The March of Folly" (1984), Barbara Tuchman[65] equates "ignoring the [i]interest of, and [ii]information held by key stakeholders" to folly; she suggests that it has led to disaster, from Troy to Vietnam, and to the failure of many large projects!

There is no more excuse for project practitioners getting confused about the purposes of Stakeholder Management or for just going through the motions of whatever SM process is imposed on them, or hoping to put some *would-be* stakeholders to sleep till the project is done – It is unambiguously clear what purposes SM will seek to achieve:

(1) Securing relevant input (e.g., requirements) into the project delivery processes;
(2) Securing buy-in (i.e., support for a winning coalition) on the part of the various role-players (i.e., whose interests are at stake) within the project environment.

In addition to gathering *relevant input* from key, pertinent stakeholders, a structured Stakeholder Management will equally seek (i.e., by engagement) to secure *dependable buy-in* from various role-players, both internal and external. This is achieved through a delicate balancing of "forces" of power, politics, interest, and influence emanating from different (or differing) parties. Securing input and securing buy-in go hand in hand. There is no better (winning) coalition than stakeholders identifying themselves with the project; "People support what they create, and resist what they're excluded from".[68]

It flows from the foregoing that any "uncertainty" in securing *stakeholder input* and/or *buy-in* in terms of project objectives will constitute a "risk" to the project outcomes!

Therein arises the realisation that any inadequate or failed Stakeholder Management has the potential to cause a large and complex project (e.g., Large Infrastructure Projects, LIPs) to fail. This should convince even the most stubborn of project practitioners that SM is definitely not a *side-dish*, delegated to a junior team member to "deal with the people out there!"

Having understood the real purposes of SM (i.e., not about *mesmerising* some vocal antagonists), the project manager relies on SM processes to, let us say, identify relevant stakeholders from which "system requirements" should be elicited. Moreover, should a dependable buy-in be secured through suitable engagements of stakeholders, the project manager will also enjoy the benefits of having stakeholders actually supporting and promoting the project – and its outcomes (e.g., its products). This is markedly true in LIPs due to their scale and complexity; LIPs entail a multiplicity of contexts, involving stakeholders in the *broader* environment.

In fact, Principle 16 of the King IV Code of Governance (South Africa) states, "In the execution of its governance role and responsibilities, the governing body [e.g., board of directors] should adopt a stakeholder-inclusive approach that balances the needs, interests and expectations of material stakeholders in the best interests of the organisation over time".

Bourne (2009)[11] takes a radical stance regarding Stakeholder Management by asking, "Can an organisational activity deliver its outcome on time and on budget and still be considered a failure, despite delivering 100% of its scope?"; she argues,

> The answer must be, "Yes, it can, because people [i.e. the project stakeholders] are the key to success or failure!" Other factors can influence the perception (and possible reality) of how successful an activity may be. The process of building Heathrow's Terminal 5 and its public opening in 2008 is a good example of how different stakeholders will have conflicting perceptions of success (or failure) depending on their experiences and expectations, and how the passage of time may also affect stakeholders' perceptions.

Furthermore, PMBoK (2013)[47] suggests that Stakeholder Management should (and indeed does) "interconnect" with other critical project delivery processes as follows:

(a) "Project governance – the alignment of the project with stakeholders' needs or objectives – is critical to the successful management of stakeholder engagement and the achievement of organizational objectives .... It provides a framework in which the project manager and sponsors can make decisions that satisfy both stakeholder needs and expectations and organizational strategic objectives or address circumstances where these may not be in alignment" – Stakeholder Management supports, but also relies on effective project governance processes!

The two purposes of Stakeholder Management, namely the securing of *relevant* input and the securing of *dependable* buy-in, make it necessary (albeit not sufficient) to embed this practice onto the approved project lifecycle methodologies, which then make it a governance requirement, as it were, aimed at preventing failures.

On the other hand, the practical application of Stakeholder Management in itself also supports project governance in the sense that the input secured from the various relevant stakeholders will enhance the decision-making process by assuring the needs and expectations of key stakeholders are taken into account. Hence, "collaborative governance" is required between project managers and sponsors[34] and the symbiotic relation between SM and project governance is worth nurturing.

(b) "While operations management is different from project management ... the needs of stakeholders who perform and conduct business operations are important considerations [i.e., input] in projects that will affect their future work and endeavors. Project managers who consider and appropriately include operational stakeholders in all phases of projects, gain insight and avoid unnecessary issues that often arise when their input is overlooked" — Stakeholder Management supports and *actively* promotes Operational Readiness processes!

Projects are primarily about improving the operational environment. Regrettably, many satisfactorily completed "systems" (e.g., aircrafts, mine shafts, power plants, road and rail networks, hospitals, and schools completed on time, on budget, and to specifications) are often failing to add value by providing improvements to their intended operational environment. Operational Readiness is essential for success.

It thus becomes crucial that operational requirements (i.e., input) are elicited from relevant stakeholders and that role-players in the operational environment are in support of the project (i.e., buy-in), both in terms of its delivery and final outcomes – no project should ever see the light of day unless it adds value to operations!

(c) Figure 1.2 implies SM activities should be treated in the same way as other "core" project activities; however, it is scant on aspects such as (1) multiplicity of contexts, (2) network of agents, and (3) emergence, which are all *crucial* in addressing complexity!

This process diagram eloquently shows how "Stakeholder Engagement" is *intrinsically* linked to critical project management processes such as the Project Management Plan, Monitoring and Control, and Documentation Management, just to name a few. It follows that Stakeholder Management activities should be managed at the same level of definition and with the same diligence as the above-mentioned PM Processes – or any other activities as required by the project lifecycle methodology. Any form of asymmetry between SM processes and other activities will prove fatal.

Moreover, in the environment of complexity (which applies to LIPs), both the SM process and any other project planning and

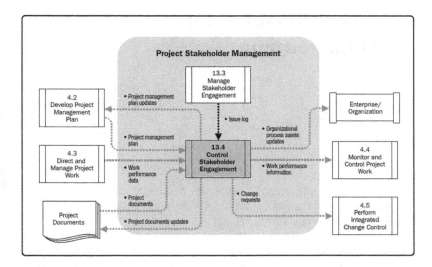

Figure 1.2 Stakeholder Engagement Process, as per PMBoK[47]

delivery process needs to be considered from a Systems Thinking (ST) perspective that caters for the dynamic aspects pertaining to "relationships" and "emergent" behaviours. (*ST is a discipline for seeing wholes. It is a framework for seeing interrelationships rather than things, for seeing patterns of change rather than static "snapshots"*[34])

2 Failed Stakeholder Management

Stakeholder Management (SM) emerges from the universal (common law) principle of "Hear the other side"; examples of its application can be found as early as the 1700s.

> Nineteenth and early twentieth century decisions established that the right to be heard (*AUDI ALTERAM PARTEM*) rule was to govern the conduct of arbitrators, of professional bodies and voluntary associations in the exercise of their disciplinary functions, and indeed of every tribunal or body of persons invested with authority [e.g., project managers] to adjudicate upon matters involving civil consequences to individuals [in projects].[62]

And Jesus plainly told an "expert in the law": "Love your neighbour [i.e., the other party] as yourself"; like the man, project managers still ask: "Who is my neighbour?" [Luke 10:25–29].

Despite the early adoption of the *Audi Alteram Partem* rule, recent history is replete with examples of projects running into complications and/ or failure due to flawed SM:

(i) The SASOL (South Africa) proposal to develop a new coal mine on the south bank of the Vaal River near Sasolburg during the 1990s was shelved and has still not been implemented due to "stakeholder opposition" (legal action by neighbours).[18]

(ii) Betuweroute (Holland):

> In the early stages, the project delivery organisation focused on the 'route decision' ... Stakeholder management was not a main issue ... This created a massive opposition towards the project

and led to severe scope changes and cost increases. These experiences of the Betuweroute showed that the traditional internal management style was not appropriate and that new ways should be found ... After this period of lessons learnt, from the mid 90's, the importance of managing stakeholders was taken seriously and the open approach became a best practice.[43]

Flawed SM had put the success of the project at risk.

(iii)   Heathrow Airport Terminal 5 (UK£4.3 bn):

> has been acknowledged as the 'most successful UK construction project' due to innovative project management practices which focused on collaboration ... T5 was officially opened on 14 March ... began operating on 27 March, 2008. From the first day flights had to be cancelled, passengers were stranded, and over 15,000 pieces of baggage were lost ... Its failure was a failure to manage the people side – poor preparation of the people responsible for operation of the facility ... indicated by the failure to prepare the staff [i.e., internal stakeholders] for the immense changes of working within the new building and its infrastructure, to involve staff through adequate training and include contingencies on the first couple of days of operation.[12]

Many Large Infrastructure Projects (LIPs) focus on applying "Technical Practices" to prevent and/or address "physical" flaws – only representing the proverbial *tip of the iceberg* (Figure 2.1)!

Due to the complexity of LIPs (i.e., essentially being technological systems "nested" in the socio-economic environment), it is not always obvious how an inadequate or failed SM implementation might have caused a project to fail. An examination of the following examples of "abandoned malls"[64] (i.e., project failures) reveals incidences of failed Stakeholder Management issues (Table 2.1).

In most of the cited examples, the shopping mall's demise was not caused by a failure of engineering or of project management in terms of the technical delivery (i.e., completing project on time, on budget, and to specifications). It generally happened due to a failure to address SM issues during Development, or later on during Operations.

The examples of projects (see Table 2.1) that failed due to an inadequate or lack of SM should suffice to dispel "myths" that are still prevalent in LIPs as follows:

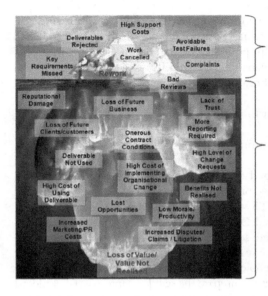

Many project teams, sponsors seem to only address "physical" defects that affect the products and/or outcome(s) of their project – but often to no avail!

Most of these "physical" defects and flaws are symptom(s) of some "deep-rooted" shortcomings, many of which [1] arose from non-technical or "soft" problems, and [2] have triggered manifestations that proper Stakeholder Management (SM) processes could have addressed!

Therefore, "Value" that is lost, forfeited through inadequate or lack of SM processes will almost never be retrieved by technical "Rework" attempts!

Figure 2.1 Project issues from an Iceberg perspective, adapted from Mosaic[13]

(1) Stakeholders are essentially external, remote from the project environment. *Over and over, it has proved a costly mistake to ignore and discard stakeholders on the basis that they had nothing to offer to the project, as mere spectators to it – overlooking "negative" stakeholders can result in a higher likelihood of failure.*

(2) Stakeholder Management is part of an Environmental Impact Assessment (EIA). *The EIA process is about determining to what extent the project will affect the natural environment (e.g., land) and its biodiversity (i.e., people, flora fauna). However, the EIA is but a component that feeds into SM, which is much broader.*

(3) Stakeholder Management is achieved through a *generic* Communication Plan. *Although a Communication Plan is an essential part of Stakeholder Management, not the other way round, it is worth noting that such a plan should flow from a specific (not generic) strategy as to how to engage stakeholders in the project. The Communication Plan focuses on an "exchange of information" among parties.*

(4) Stakeholders are all the same, and behave in the same manner, in any projects. *Every project is "unique", has its specific context, and entails peculiar dynamics – all of which affects a different set of stakeholders, each time in different ways. (list continues on page 13)*

Table 2.1 Ten abandoned malls worth exploring, as per TopTenz[64]

Shopping mall explored	Failure storyline, as extracted from the video's narrative
01 Randall Park Mall (Cleveland, USA)	The well-planned and easily accessible Randall Park opened in 1976 to great anticipation and celebration. It had major potential and at the time was one of the largest malls ever built. *Its popularity began declining following the establishment of a rival centre that stole most of Randall's upscale customers.* Falling sales prompted shop-owners to shut down; *an incident where a suspected shoplifter was fatally injured by mall security did not help its reputation.* Randall Park shut its doors for good in 2009 while reports in 2014 suggested that the mall will be destroyed to make way for industrial buildings.
02 Cloverleaf Mall (Virginia, USA)	The mall was opened in 1972 to serve as the epicentre of the area's fashion community. While the mall and its initial 45 stores enjoyed unparalleled success in its heyday, its popularity was at the end by the 1990s. *The mall developed a reputation for attracting kids in baggy pants in chained belts – and worst of all, attracting gang members.* While fears were mostly overblown, *the mall's reputation went down the drain when the rumours came through – in 1996, two clerks were murdered in a robbery.*
03 Greeley Mall (Colorado, USA)	The mall was open to the masses in 1973 and went strong during the 1980s and 1990s. In 2004, new capital was injected into the mall for renovations; interiors were redone, skylights were added, and a new theatre was installed. *Things were looking up until the sudden closure of major clothing stores followed by the opening of a new mall in the nearby neighbourhood drove off most of their customers.* The mall has not been able to stand as proudly as it once did, and *foot traffic has been down to a minimum.* The decline caused the mall to be sold many times over the years; most notably the mall was sold for US$6.1 million in 2012, a sharp decline from 2006's estimated value of US$41 million.
04 New World Mall (Bangkok, Thailand)	The mall never saw the light at the end of the tunnel. *Work on the ambitious 11-storey project begun in the 1980s but when the construction company was found guilty of breaching building law, work immediately halted and the mall was shut down.* The abandoned mall currently serves as a humongous fish-tank for a wide variety of sea creatures. How? ... the roof was not completed and the basement accumulated enough stagnant rain water to breed mosquitoes; *this caused terrible annoyance to locals who decided to release fish into the water to stop the mosquitoes from breeding but the fish started to breed instead.*

(Continued)

Table 2.1 Continued

Shopping mall explored	Failure storyline, as extracted from the video's narrative
05 Sobey's Square (Newfoundland, Canada)	Mount Pearl Sobey's Square was built after *the largest city of Saint Johns denied access that might have given it a different fortune.* They went through a major renovation in the 1990s but all that effort that went into the expansion turned out to be fruitless. *In order to curb further losses, shops started closing down one after the other;* currently, only movie theatres are still operating successfully.
06 Brookside Mall (Fredericton, Canada)	Established in the late 1970s but *it no longer satisfies the need of consumers.* It was built with the intent of attracting both north and south sides of the town, but after it opened, it was like a peanut compared to the humongous mall of today. The fortunes of the 20-store shopping centre started spiralling downward *following the construction of a rival mall three times the size.* Brookside followed suit and tried to expand with the times but to no success; the mall is currently enduring a slow death.
07 The Glenfield Westfield Mall (Auckland, New Zealand)	The Glenfield Westfield Mall is famous for the extensive upgrade it went through. The Westfield Mall Chain bought the Glenfield Mall in 1996 and spent US$100 million to modernise the mall in 2000. The mall stood the test of time for around six years *but after the new mall scent wore off it couldn't keep up with the introduction of a rival shopping centre. All their high-end clothing brands jumped on the bandwagon and established their base in upcoming malls.* Everything about the Glenfield Mall is out of date and any future upgrade is an unlikely possibility.
08 Tallahassee Mall (Florida, USA)	The Tallahassee Mall first saw light in 1971 when it opened with the anchor-stores of Willco, Gapefirz, and Montgomery Ward. *Currently only a handful of stores are in breakeven; the rest are all losing their investors buckets of money.* Although the mall was foreclosed in January 2011, a real estate company jumped at the opportunity to pay the mall's lease only a month later. Although the mall is functioning, it needs to start punching above its weight if it wants to see another decade.

(*Continued*)

Table 2.1 Continued

Shopping mall explored	Failure storyline, as extracted from the video's narrative
09 El Con Center (Arizona, USA)	The oldest mall in Tuscan is on life-support; it was established in 1960 as an outdoor shopping centre *but it is no longer the heartbeat of the town as it currently remains home to only a handful of stores.* The entire north-west wing faced demolition in 1998. *Although many retailers and restaurants opened in the 2000s, the mall lost tenants in equal numbers.* In 2011, some of the remaining buildings were demolished to make way for a pathway to make it easier to reach the few shops that are still operational.
10 New China Mall (Dongguan, China)	Apparently, Chinese companies have a lot of cash to burn. New South China Mall has the potential to host around 2350 stores in its 600,000 square feet *but around 80% of the mall is yet to be occupied.* The mall has been almost entirely vacant since its 2005 opening, even though Dongguan was thought to be the ideal location for a mall of its size. *The suburbs of Dongguan are only reachable by car or bus, essentially placing it in a no-man's land.* The man who spear-headed the ambitious project was Hu Guy Wong, a billionaire who made his mark in the commercial world through instant noodles.

(5) Stakeholder Management is an "off-line" practice and is not part of core delivery. *The very purposes of Stakeholder Management (as discussed in Chapter 1) would be counterintuitive if treating it as a side dish; the project itself could be at risk.*

(6) Stakeholder Management is mainly required during the "Construction" phase. *While a broader engagement is needed in terms of "harm during Construction", conducting SM from early phases is proper and necessary (i.e., to secure input).*

(7) Stakeholder Management is *largely* the responsibility of the Contractor(s). *Even during the Construction phase of the project, while broader engagements take place in and around site, many other stakeholders still need to be managed.*

The below depiction (Figure 2.2) displays the spectrum from tension to written communication to telephonic contacts and ultimately to

Figure 2.2 Stakeholder Engagement Continuum

face-to-face engagements leading to harmony. When properly implemented, SM allows role-players to move from a place of tension to a place of harmony. It basically dissipates any "entropy" in the project environment, that is:

> An amount of disorder present in a team-system that causes dispersal of energy, triggering the tendency in the team-system that is left to itself to descend into chaos; a measure of the amount of energy in a system that cannot be used to do project work.

3 Stakeholder Management and project complexity

The complexity of a "system" (e.g., power plant, rail/road network, hospital) is largely determined by the number of its parts or activities, the degree of differentiation between the parts, and the structure and strength of their connections. Moreover, complex "systems" have multiple interacting components whose collective behaviour cannot simply be inferred from the behaviours of their individual components.[24]

According to Wood:

> It is a common statement that the construction industry process is one of the most complex and risky businesses undertaken, however it has also been suggested that the construction industry has developed great difficulty in coping with the increasing complexity of major construction projects[71] – and Watt[67] definitively agrees!

Indeed, while project complexity is but one dimension of attaining project success, Baccarini still maintains "The significance of project complexity to project success or otherwise cannot be underestimated, hence the compelling need to allow for a thorough understanding of the inherent complexities in an infrastructure delivery system".[6]

> A project can be said to be complex if it consists of many interdependent parts, each of which can change in ways that are not totally predictable, and which can then have unpredictable impacts on other elements that are themselves capable of change.[15]

Large Infrastructure Projects (LIPs) fit this definition due to their scale and for being *nested* in socio-economic contexts.

On the other hand, still on account of complexity, Sussman[59, 60] refers to "Complex, Large-Scale, Interconnected, Open, Sociotechnical" as CLIOS, a class of engineering systems with a wide-ranging social and environmental impacts due to their "nested complexity". This occurs when a physical domain is nested within and interacts with an institutional sphere, where both entities are deemed complex. From that perspective, most LIPs are basically CLIOS, which again raises the issue of Stakeholder Management (SM).

It transpires from the above that not only the management of stakeholders in LIPs proves systematic (i.e., well structured), but ought to follow a systemic approach (i.e., Systems Thinking) in order to accommodate their growing complexity – or else its breakdown will trigger negative ripple effects and failure in such projects.

LIPs Delivery shall consider the *number* of activities/stakeholders (e.g., scale, number of engineering disciplines, number of suppliers and vendors) and the *relationships* among or across themselves and with the project environment. Thus, the notions of Complex Adaptive Systems, multiple causality, connectivity, emergence, and lifecycle applies!

> CAS [i.e., Complex Adaptive Systems] are organizations which perform in network composed of various agents [e.g., LIPs] ... These agents [i.e., stakeholders] learn and adapt their behaviors from the selection pressures present in the situation. The global behavior of the system [i.e., network of stakeholders] emerges, then, as the effect of the non-linear combination of the interactions among the diverse components [i.e., (groupings of) stakeholders].[19]

In LIPs, SM should consider networks of stakeholders.

Therefore, Stakeholder Management inherently "analyses the construction process, the production system and the industry, as well as the social systems formed by humans [or stakeholders] involved in the project execution [i.e., LIPs] from a complexity perspective using a number of general characteristics of complex systems".[10]

It thus follows that a Stakeholder Management process is needed in both the project environment (where systems are created and delivered) and the operational environment (where systems are to be deployed), considering such a deployment might affect both "business/operational" and "broader" environments. As suggested above, "the slightest breakdown in any of those areas will cause a negative ripple throughout the project" and project failure might ensue. If still in doubt, ask the owner of the South China Mall.

For that, Stakeholder Management shall enhance traditional, "technical" approaches. LIPs are Socio-Technological Systems:

> The combination of [i]technical ... and [ii]social sciences ... has created a dual approach in which the well-developed project oriented

approach focusing on project leadership, planning and financial engineering is combined with a social sciences approach that is focusing much more on the complex process of implementation and the variety of stakeholders.[43]

The two approaches are required!

From the first approach we can learn how to manage a project in such a way that cost overrun and delay can be mitigated. From the second approach, we can learn how adaptive managers have to be and can be in order to create effective progress in complex processes of implementation. Stakeholder management and reliable communication towards the shareholders as well as with the stakeholder are crucial criteria for success. The combination of these two approaches can help managers of infrastructure projects [e.g., LIPs] as well as the sponsors ... to deal with implementation problems, which will always appear in these complex processes.

Prof Dr Ing Geert R. Teisman[43]

In such an environment of complexity, building on the work of Scott[51] and others, the Systems Engineering (SE)-Based Approach to Stakeholder Management (SM) should apply by evoking a number of SE principles as follows:

(1) Stakeholders should be actively managed throughout the entire "System" lifecycle.

One important implication of applying Systems Engineering concepts and principles to enhance project lifecycle methodologies (PLM) entails a lifecycle that reflects an Operational Environment. This emerges from the understanding that projects are primarily about improving the business and/or operational environment, a notion that extends the responsibility of project teams (thus, linking project success) to improvements (or lack thereof) that occur during operations. The whole idea is that the entire project team starts the project with the end (i.e., improvements in operations) in mind – which is a Systems Engineering principle.[34, 40, 47]

Merrow[40] has extensively discussed the Independent Project Analysts (IPA) project lifecycle model, rightly putting a strong emphasis on the notion of Front End Loading (FEL); thus, making a welcome departure from the "jump-straight-into-execution" tendencies that typified the traditional school of delivery. However, the IPA model is silent on vital SE practices such as Operations (it raises

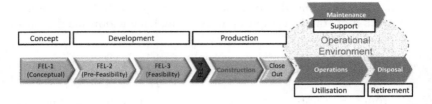

Figure 3.1 Project lifecycle in accordance with ISO 15288, by the author[34]

operational readiness issues, though), Maintenance, and Disposal – stakeholders in those spheres might be overlocked (see Figure 3.1).

In line with the above lifecycle, project stakeholders should be managed from the Conceptual phase through to Construction, Close-out, and Operations and Disposal. For that reason, "Deliverers of capital assets must actively engage the community of operations and maintenance to secure the critical operational input".[34]

These lifecycle phases usually include stakeholders with different profiles, and with needs and expectations that change as the project proceeds through the lifecycle.

Financiers/sponsors will, for instance, play a critical role during Feasibility, whereas the community around the sites will be affected during the Construction phase. Likewise, the operation team might only provide operational requirements input during the study phases but will have to play a more active role during Utilisation.

Stakeholders will not be the same, have the same needs, or behave the same way!

(2) In a SE "white paper" titled, "9 Laws of Effective Systems Engineering", Scott[51] states as Systems Engineering Law No 9 that Systems Come in 3s: "Every system design involves three systems: The system being designed [i.e. Solution-System], the system it will 'live' in [i.e. Context-System], and the system used by the team to design it [i.e. Realisation-System]".

On the other hand, Martin had written a seminal paper titled, "The Seven Samurai of Systems Engineering: Dealing with the Complexity of 7 Interrelated Systems", which he presented at the 2004 INCOSE Symposium. It suggests that the Intervention System (referred to as the Solution System) could actually "morph" into a Deployed System once installed in the Context System (which might as well become a Modified System), and would have to deal with a Collaborating System and a Sustaining System, as well as having to contend with a Competing System.[37]

Project stakeholders should be managed in these seven "Systems-of-Interest" and the requirements from such project agents should be incorporated in Design and Development of the Solution System (i.e., Intervention System), considering:

(a) **Intervention System** – *consists of the intended Solution to the Problem (P1)*;

(b) **Context System** – *where the Problem resides, also where the "Solution" will live*;

(c) **Realisation System** – *resources needed to deliver the Intervention System*;

(d) **Deployed System** – *Intervention System as morphed in the Context System*;

(e) **Collaborating System(s)** – *system(s) collaborating with the Deployed System*;

(f) **Sustaining System(s)** – *system(s) needed to sustain the Deployed System*;

(g) **Competing System(s)** – *system(s) vying for resources with the Deployed System.*

These seven individual "systems", in their totality, constitute a useful rendition of the project ecology. Each individual "system" will entail agents (i.e., stakeholders) and set of relationships among them (i.e., networks). Moreover, the higher-level connections and the dynamics among the "systems" themselves will also establish "linkages" between agents across individual "systems" (i.e., network of networks).

Any "interventions" in one "system", Senge[53] argues, could create vulnerabilities (i.e., threats) and possibilities (i.e., opportunities), and thus "create" stakeholders in other individual "systems" – but not always in close proximity of time or space.

Thus, the overall behaviour emerging from this complex ecology not only depends on the behaviours of individual stakeholders within any individual "system", but also on their *relationships* within that "system" – and across in adjacent "systems" (see Figure 3.2).

This kind of project ecology (which arises from Systems Thinking concepts) assists the project manager in identifying project stakeholders that otherwise might have been overlooked when only focusing on those entities and individuals "who are actively involved in the project or whose interest may be positively and negatively affected by the performance or the [physical] completion of the project".

More often than not, there will be entities and individuals (i.e., stakeholders) that will not only be "actively involved" in other spheres of the project ecology, but more importantly, albeit rather

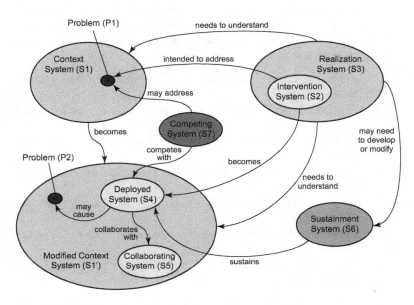

Figure 3.2 The seven Systems–of–Interest, as per Martin[37]

indirectly, "whose interest may be positively and negatively affected by the outcomes of the project". For the outcomes of projects generally endure (with their impacts persisting) much longer than whatever effect that might come about during "the performance or the completion of the project".

The reality of LIPs suggests that those "outcomes" generally manifest in all seven aforementioned "Systems-of-Interest", making relevant the stakeholders therein.

(3) The Systems-of-Systems (SoS) context adds a level of complexity to the management of stakeholders.

SoS are defined as "interoperating collection of component systems that produce results unachievable by individual systems alone",[32] "a collection of 'independently useful' systems that delivers 'unique' capabilities".

The US Department of Defense published a SE Guide for Systems-of-Systems; it provides guidance regarding the management of stakeholders in a SoS situation:

> One aspect of the environment that affects the SE process is the community [i.e., group of interacting stakeholders] in which a

system or SoS is developed and deployed. Generally, for a single system, stakeholders are committed to that system and play specific roles in the SE of that system ...

On the other hand, for SoS, there are stakeholders for both the SoS and for the constituent systems themselves. These stakeholder groups each have their own objectives and organizational contexts which form their expectations with respect to the SoS. The stakeholders of the SoS may have limited knowledge of the constraints and development plans for the individual systems.

In some cases, every SoS stakeholder may not be recognized. Stakeholders of individual systems may have little interest in the SoS, may give SoS needs low priority, or may resist SoS demands on their [independently functional] system. These competing stakeholder interests establish the complex stakeholder environment for SoS SE.[44]

Conflating system-level and SoS-level stakeholders will prove counterproductive, as the paragraph above explains. While stakeholders could still remain connected from one level to the other, it must always be kept in mind that agents in either sphere do not necessarily share the same objectives and therefore will not behave the same. They will not have the same needs nor provide/request the same input!

Consider the case of an Integrated Transit System to rationalise and connect public transport "systems" in a world-class city. This *integrated* "system" (consisting of buses, trains, local airlines, and hotel services) is actually a SoS in its own right.

SoS-level stakeholders who are interested in enjoying seamless transits, reduced tariffs, and safety would not share the concerns of hotel management who are struggling with occupancy rate, especially during the winter off-peak season. Likewise, train operators (as agents in a single "system") would not necessarily agree to cross-subsidising bus rides in a bid to make the round-transit affordable.

(4) Systems Thinking (ST) and Soft Systems Methodologies (SSM or CLIOS) should be used in managing project stakeholders, considering, as stated above, that LIPs are actually "Technological" Systems that are *nested* in "Socio-economic" Systems:

Where decision problems are more complex and cannot be easily defined by decision-makers, rational methods [i.e., traditional SM] are more difficult to apply. Such [wicked] problems involve solving a set of interlocking issues and constraints by multiple stakeholders. A set of auxiliary management tools are required by [agent-] groups engaged in project definition to help manage such complexity.[69]

One such tool in the application of SSM is to address the seemingly wicked problem of elucidating the owner's requirements at the earliest stages of the project lifecycle at a point when both problems and solutions are intrinsically nebulous, and therefore are hard even to formulate. Wicked problems are systematic problems that are typified by multiple stakeholders involved in complex and unpredictable interactions, where both the problem and the solution to it are unknown until a kind of "solution" is first proposed, and where understanding of motivations, viewpoints, and interactions and addressing both qualitative and quantitative dimensions of the situation are required.[69, 70]

Before giving an overview of SSM, Maqsood defined what wicked problems are: "Wicked problems typically have a dense web of inter-related factors, making it very difficult to understand how one decision will impact decisions in other areas. This class of problem often exists in dynamic and uncertain environments that generate significant risk".[36] This definition fits the context of stakeholders in LIPs. Likewise, Becker[8] observes that conflict arises (i.e., among stakeholders) from wicked problems where there are competing claims, especially where "good outcomes" are traded off against "bad outcomes" within the same "value system".

Not only is there a basket of potential alternative criteria [i.e., a wicked problem], the judgement can be made by a wide range of potential stakeholders, over different time horizons. Project success could even be defined as: "The satisfaction of all stakeholders". Perceiving project success simply as the compliance of time, finance and quality constraints can be described as a more "narrow" view in this respect ... The context, especially changes in context such as for example a change in government or new demands regarding safety, can heavily influence both the results and the organisation of a project.[43]

NETLIPSE observed this in 15 LIPs.

In terms of the proposed SE-Based Approach to SM, project stakeholders will be located within (and have *relationships* across) various individual "systems" of the project ecology. The author proposes a model with two tiers (i.e., macroscopic systems and microscopic systems), depending on "project objectives" to define which individual "systems" apply.

Further, consistent with the work of Scott ("Systems Come in 3s"),[51] LIPs will consider component "systems" from where stakeholders shall be identified and actively managed; these are (1) Solution System (i.e., the system being designed); (2) Realisation System (i.e., the system used by the team to design it); and (3) Context System (i.e., the system it will "live" in).

Depending on the scale, the scope (i.e., which "systems" are involved), and complexity of the project, specific "components" of the project ecology become pertinent. Accordingly, stakeholders will have to be managed in those spheres for project success. Figure 3.3 summarises the main elements of an ecology for Large Infrastructure Projects. In practice, only those that prove pertinent should be retained for the SM process.

When it comes to small to medium projects, the need to embrace a Systems Thinking approach to managing stakeholders might not always arise; their size and relative simplicity allows such projects to get away with a traditional or limited perspective of Stakeholder Management.

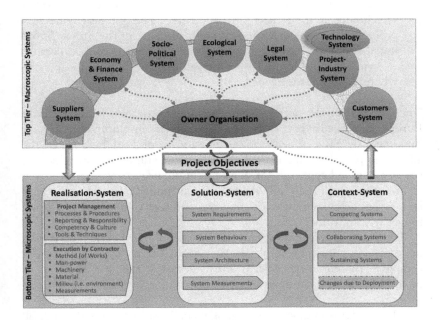

Figure 3.3 Project ecology for Large Infrastructure Projects (LIPs)

Nevertheless, in large and complex projects such as megaprojects (i.e., LIPs) there is always a compelling need to consider the full horizon of the multiplicity of contexts surrounding that particular project. A failure to abide by this provision will create risks to the project.

Hertogh, the NETLIPSE Project Manager, declares that as important as implementing a risk management that focuses on threats may be, it is not sufficient.[43] Risk management should also focus on opportunities, which are the result of interacting with relevant stakeholders – and they are identified across the whole project lifecycle and its ecology.

Merrow gives the example of a serious illness for the local population that was not identified and mitigated to explain how "the failure to identify a set of stakeholders can have tragic implications". Indeed, history suggests that the first real attempt to build the Panama Canal was by the French (circa 1880), led by Ferdinand de Lesseps using the experience from the Suez Canal (successfully completed in 1869). The attempt, however, was cancelled in 1893 due to the high death rate from yellow fever and malaria among the workers, resulting in huge losses for the private and public investors.[40]

Stakeholder Management determines project success.

> Successful projects involve the customer, users, operators, and other stakeholders in the project development ... The systems engineering process includes stakeholders through all stages of the project, from initial needs definition through system verification and acceptance ... with an opportunity to contribute to the steps in the process where their input is needed.[50]

The NETLIPSE Report (2008), having investigated 15 LIPs across Europe, remarked: "It is clear that stakeholders should be seen as very important by project delivery organisations, not least because of the adverse impact that stakeholders can have on the timescales for achieving the consents and approvals for work to commence".[43]

Still, the report sadly observed, "only in limited cases from the projects researched was stakeholder management seen to be a pro-active and longer term priority".[43]

The secret to *holistically* approaching Stakeholder Management resides in considering project role-players (i.e., agents) across the whole project ecology – the entire lifecycle. Ryen suggests this is one of the ways to build "Intelligent Transportation Systems":

> The systems engineering process includes stakeholders through all stages of the project, from initial needs definition through system

verification and acceptance ... with an opportunity to contribute to the steps in the process where their input is needed.[50]

This lifecycle perspective is confirmed in ISO 15288 (Standard on Systems Lifecycle) as it considers "systems that are man–made, created and utilised to provide products and/or services in defined environment for the benefits of users and other stakeholders".[32]

A further confirmation has come from no other place than the SEBoK Online Portal,[52] "Stakeholders of a SoI may vary throughout the lifecycle. Thus, in order to get a complete set of needs and subsequent requirements, it is important to consider all stages of the lifecycle when identifying the stakeholders or classes of stakeholders".

Management of stakeholders in itself may add to the *inherent* complexity of the system. Sussman[60] submits that a "complex" system that is composed of a group of interrelated components and subsystems for which the degree and nature of the relationships between them is imperfectly known, with varying directionality, magnitude, and timescales of interactions, could present various types of complexity as follows:

(i)   Structural Complexity – a type that concerns itself with the Product.
      Exists when the system consists of a large number of interconnected parts;
(ii) Behavioural complexity – a type that concerns itself with the Product.
      Exists when predictions of system outputs or behaviour are difficult. This is found when their parts interact over time in closely coupled feedback loops;
(iii) Nested Complexity – which concerns itself with the Environment.
      It is a concept that suggests a complex "physical/technical" system embedded within an institutional (i.e., socio-economic) system;
(iv) Evaluative Complexity – a type that concerns itself with the Environment.
      Reflects multi-stakeholder environments in which Complex Systems exist.

The last two types of complexities, namely types (iii) and (iv), are strongly related to the various stakeholders in the project ecology and how they might behave through the project lifecycle – both during project delivery and subsequently during Operations.

To put it in a nutshell, not only Stakeholder Management itself will become complex in an environment of complexity, but it may also contribute to such a complexity. For this compelling reason, Stakeholder Management should be approached in the system way.

4   Four–Step Approach to managing stakeholders

Vijay S. Shukla from the QBI Institute (India) argues: "For project success good relationship and rapport with your stakeholders is necessary, but not a *sufficient* condition".[54]

In fact, it is clear from previous chapters that Stakeholder Management in Large Infrastructure Projects (LIPs) is far too important (i.e., potential to cause project failure), convoluted (i.e., applies to several parts of the project ecology and lifecycle), and downright complex (i.e., capable of compounding complexity and displaying emerging behaviours) to be approached in a random, haphazard manner. It has to be systematic!

Both practitioners and academia support this need for a "structured approach":

> One of the first things that a project manager should therefore do is to [i]identify all the stakeholders, [ii]determine their needs as well as their expectations, and [iii]resolve conflicts. If this is not done, a large number of disruptive changes could be expected at a later stage.[58]

This kind of "step-by-step" approach should form the basis of any structured (i.e., systematic) and systemic (i.e., based on Systems Thinking) framework for managing stakeholders in LIPs. However, it seems to miss one very crucial "step": The preparation in terms of strategy and planning that goes before "*resolving conflicts*".

Relying merely on *intuition* or prior experience in managing project stakeholders could prove misleading (even hazardous and fatal to projects). A "structured approach" to managing stakeholder is required to ensure that all issues are taken into consideration.

"Management is the use of limited resources to achieve predetermined specific goals". Managing project stakeholders is like managing any "organisation", except that it gets more involved, as discussed previously.

In defining an organisation as "Any structured group brought together to achieve certain goals that the individuals could not reach alone",[26] Stakeholder Management includes four management functions:

(1) Planning – defining goals and putting in place ways/means of reaching them;
(2) Organising – creating a structure of relationships to enable the reaching of goals;
(3) Leading – communicating and motivating to perform tasks for achieving goals;
(4) Controlling – deliberately monitoring "actions" and correcting performance.

It transpires from the foregoing that whatever "structured approach" will be proposed for Stakeholder Management (SM) should in essence abide by these four organisational requirements and, for a reason, prove capable of dealing with the complexities involved.

The *generic* "structured approached" above by Steyn[58] satisfies these requirements, provided suitable accommodation is made regarding the "strategy and planning" step, which is achieved by expanding on the very definition provided by PMBoK as follows:

The processes required [1]to identify the people, groups, or organizations that could impact or be impacted by the project, [2]to analyze stakeholder expectations [and claims] and their impact on the project, and [3]to develop appropriate management strategies for [4]effectively engaging stakeholders in project decisions and execution.[47]

Therefore, without forsaking the element of "Leading" since "leadership" is *similarly* essential in managing stakeholders, SM should concern itself with the following steps:

(1) Identifying stakeholders – to determine "who" the project stakeholders might be;
(2) Analysing stakeholders' stakes and "claims" and their "intersecting" relationships;
(3) Developing a Strategy and a Plan for engaging and involving the stakeholders;
(4) Implementing the Strategy (while maintaining and updating both Strategy and Plan) by engaging and involving the various stakeholders throughout the lifecycle (see Figure 4.1 below).

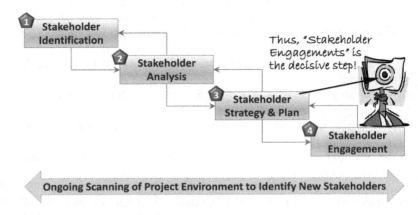

Figure 4.1 Four-Step Stakeholder Management Approach, as per the author

These elements are the bedrock of the Four-Step Approach to Stakeholder Management. They somewhat differ from the PMBoK SM Process;[47] namely, (1) identify stakeholders; (2) plan Stakeholder Management; (3) manage Stakeholder Engagement; and (4) control Stakeholder Management. PMBoK step (1) comprises Analysis, and steps (3) and (4) are both about implementing Engagement; thus, the differences are mostly in arrangement.

It is quite reassuring that, except in their arrangement, the proposed Four-Step Approach to Stakeholder Management is consistent with the PMBoK. However, a discussion is needed to establish to what extent and in which way the envisaged SM steps shall comply with the demands of Systems Thinking (ST). This is needed to unravel the "complexities" afflicting megaprojects, which the existing PMBoK has not necessarily achieved so far.

INCOSE has acknowledged the complex nature of LIPs:

> In LIPs there are many complexities. There may be a number of outcomes required by a variety of stakeholders, some seemingly contrary to each other, and many alternative ways to satisfy the requirements all competing for priority and for the same resources and finances.[30]

Baccarini[6] already made this point way back in 1996, but 23 years on, the "thorough understanding" of complexities in megaprojects is yet to be attained, particularly when it comes to managing stakeholders in Large Infrastructure Projects!

Hence, each one of the four steps (and in their totality) shall pass the test of complexity:

(1) Conducting "Stakeholder Identification" in an environment of complexity.

Stakeholders should be identified across the Systems-of-Interest owing to their location within and/or proximity to either individual "system", as well as due to their relationships to elements or agents (i.e., other stakeholders) within such a "system".

(2) Conducting "Stakeholder Analysis" in an environment of complexity.

Interests, claims, and attitudes (e.g., buy-in versus hostility) as well as their likely roles and responsibilities should be explored or anticipated in line with their position and/or intersecting relationships with other stakeholders in a "dynamic" network.

(3) Conducting "Stakeholder Strategy and Planning" in an environment of complexity.

A strategy for adequate, meaningful stakeholder engagements and its execution plan should reflect non-linearity (i.e., a minor action having a major impact elsewhere).

(4) Conducting "Stakeholder Engagement" in an environment of complexity.

Stakeholders' responses to engagements should be monitored since "emergence" can cause interdependent agents to change in ways that are not totally predictable.

Besides such considerations, in line with Systems Thinking, SM should explore beyond "daily events" affecting stakeholders to analyse and anticipate any patterns and trends, as well as the systemic structure (i.e., the way in which the parts of a "system" are arranged). Indeed, Systems Thinking is especially useful for defining problems ... By shedding light on the root causes of a problem and letting you anticipate the multiple consequences of your solutions, it can help you avoid solutions that only spawn more difficulties.[23]

Moreover, one important implication of applying Systems Engineering concepts and principles to enhance project lifecycle methodologies entails a lifecycle that reflects the Operational Environment – with the understanding that projects are primarily about improving (or establishing) that particular environment (as per Chapter 3). The whole idea is that the entire project team starts the project with the end

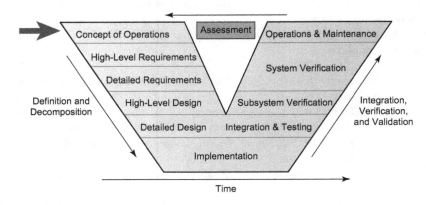

Figure 4.2 SE Vee Model, showing "Concept of Operations", ConOps[66]

(i.e., improvements in operations) in mind – which is a central Systems Engineering principle.[33, 47]

It follows that the effective identification of stakeholders and their requirements (e.g., Stakeholder Requirements), among others, shall flow from the "Concept of Operations" or System ConOps, which is viewed as part (i.e., the first step) of the SE Lifecycle Process (Figure 4.2).

The ConOps defines the "goal" (why) of the system towards the achievement of which stakeholders shall be managed and, as such, it also informs who the stakeholders are. The Concept of Operations answers the *why, who, what, when, where,* and *how* for the new (intended) "system", describes a "day-in-the-life" of the "system", and provides context to all the aspects of such a "system"; it reflects the "*who*" of the particular project.

"The ConOps describes how a community intends to use a contemplated 'system' as a means to mitigate or suppress an actual or anticipated problem situation. It serves to converge multiple stakeholders toward a common image and understanding of the requested 'system'".[56] Therefore, the ConOps document describes the desired characteristics of the "system" from the users' (and key stakeholders') viewpoint and provides identification of the environment in which the "system" will function. It serves as a vehicle to communicate the high-level quantitative and qualitative characteristics of the "system" to the user, buyer, developer, and other relevant "system stakeholder".

Regrettably, this notion has remained foreign, even to *seasoned* project practitioners.

A simple example might prove useful in explaining what could seem too complicated to understand. Consider that a young boy was driving to school every day with his father. He sometimes got annoyed that their fast and flashy red sports car would only "roar and sprint" at 120 km/hour for a stretch of the highway, but then would come to a complete standstill every time they bumped into a traffic jam. He once looked around at the sea of cars literally stuck on the highway, closed his eyes for a few seconds as if to sink in deep thoughts, and in a burst of excitement, said to his father:

> Dad, I know exactly the kind of car you need to buy. It must be able to sense the traffic jam ahead and automatically shift to an airplane mode to fly us beyond the damn jam, and then land back on the highway where you can drive at 120 km/hour again – you, Dad, will still enjoy the driving, and I will never be late to school again!

What the young boy told his father was essentially a ConOps for the envisaged car; it describes how the father would use the contemplated device to solve the traffic problem on a daily basis. Further, it defines to which context the problem will be solved. The clever boy had in fact articulated the *why, who, what, when, where,* and *how* for the intended "system". The solution to be devised would, thus, improve traffic operations!

Assuming the boy's problem could be solved through some technical or engineering means; whatever solution (e.g., a racing-flying car?) to be developed would most probably involve stakeholders beyond the domain of car manufacturing and road transportation. It would also include, among others, aviation authorities (the vehicle being a "flying object"), environmental protection agencies (depending on the type of "jet fuel" to be used), and the car insurance industry, given the changes in the "profile" of road accidents. Right here, a more holistic understanding of stakeholders (with their possible roles and responsibilities) is attained, something only made *practical* through using the ConOps.

What is good for this boy's dream car shall also be good for large and complex projects. Systems Engineering[39, 56] advises using the ConOps *as the first step* before building any piece of infrastructure item (e.g., water or power plant, mining shaft, road/rail network, shopping mall, hospital, school). This approach (refer to Vee Model in Figure 4.2) will not only assist the project team in defining the *Why* (project rationale), *What* (products/services to be delivered), its location, lifespan, and so on, it will also assist in identifying the stakeholders (and their roles and responsibilities) in various "realms" of the Systems-of-Interest, which is not easy to achieve in an environment of complexity (see Figure 4.3 below).

If anything, in showing the logical connection between Stakeholder Management and the notion of ConOps, the foregoing discourse

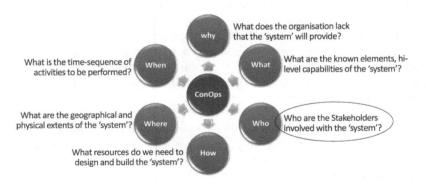

Figure 4.3 Representation of "Concept of Operations", ConOps as per Smith[56]

confirms that the two main purposes of this crucial project management process (i.e., securing of *relevant input* and securing of *dependable buy-in*) conform to the Systems Engineering principle of *beginning the project with the end (of improving operations)* in the mind of the relevant stakeholders.

By logically and traceably linking the *why* of the project to its *who* (stakeholders), the effective application, ConOps, provides assurance that the *input* (e.g., requirements) elicited from relevant stakeholders (as identified) might result in project outcomes most stakeholders would give *buy-in* to and accept to utilise in "improving operations".

> [For] ConOps is the first step in the systems engineering "Vee" – while integral throughout the entire process, its most critical, and directly related, roles will be in the direct assistance to the generation of System Requirements [i.e., input], and in System Validation once it has entered an Operations and Maintenance phase [i.e., buy-in] … One noted that the discussions among stakeholders during the Concept of Operations development were essential for the success [not failure] of the system, since all organizations came to a consensus on the vision for the project.[56]

Oh, that project practitioners will accommodate the ConOps in their SM methodology!

In a nutshell, the proposed **Four-Step Approach to Stakeholder Management** is based on three cardinal pillars in order to *effectively* deal with the complexity inherent to Large Infrastructure Projects: Structured Approach, Systems Thinking, and ConOps. The next four chapters (Chapters 5 to 8) will discuss each of these steps in details.

5 Stakeholder Identification

Failure to identify a key stakeholder can cause major problems for any project, as both common sense and experience will suggest. Hence, internal and external stakeholders should be accurately identified and correctly recorded in the Project Stakeholder Register.

Internal stakeholders (e.g., sponsors, project team members) have a *stake* in the project as a failed outcome will more often than not affect their morale, or even their career. The same goes about a company's top executives who might want to use the project to showcase their company. These two categories, and other internal role-players (e.g., other departments that might benefit or be affected), should be listed as stakeholders.

According to the Chaos Report[57], every single "cause" of project failure has (a lot) to do with Stakeholder Management. For instance, the "Lack of user input" item (13%, which is the biggest single contributor to project failure) clearly arises from a failure to identify and appreciate the users as relevant stakeholders. Likewise, "Lack of executive support" can arise from inadequate/lack of engagement with key members of the executive management. Thus, failure to identify stakeholders will cause project failure!

Identifying stakeholders and understanding their relative degree of influence on a project is critical; overlooking "positive" stakeholders denies the project of much needed support, while overlooking "negative" stakeholders will result in a higher likelihood of project failure.[1] Therefore, the Project Manager should provide the right "leadership!"

However, PMBoK makes a difference between the responsibility of the project manager and the rest of the project team as far as Stakeholder Management is concerned. PMBoK [47] states:

[1]The project team identifies internal and external, positive and negative, and performing and advising stakeholders in order to determine the project requirements and the expectations of all parties involved … [2]The project manager should manage the influences of

these various stakeholders in relation to the project requirements to ensure a successful outcome.

These roles are separated as follows:

(1)   The onus is on the project team (i.e., each and every member) to identify relevant stakeholders in order to determine the *input* that might be expected from them (i.e. requirements) or by them (i.e. information);

(2)   The project manager, on the other hand, shall remain responsible for "managing the influences of these various stakeholders ... to ensure a successful outcome". This aspect is further discussed under "Stakeholder Analysis" and ensuing chapters.

However, PMBoK cautions as follows:

Stakeholder identification is a continuous process throughout the entire project life cycle. Identifying stakeholders, understanding their relative degree of influence on a project ... are critical to the success of the project. Failure to do so can lead to delays, cost increases, unexpected issues, and other negative consequences including project cancellation. An example is late recognition that the legal department is a significant stakeholder, which results in delays and increased expenses due to legal requirements that are required to be met before the project can be completed or the product scope is delivered.[47]

Successful SM starts with a rigorous "Identification".

While PMBoK insists that "It is critical for project success to identify the stakeholders early in the project", it conspicuously fails to propose any appropriate tools. Nonetheless, several frameworks, tools, and techniques are available from the Systems Engineering and ICT circles; they should guide project practitioners in a "structured" Identification of relevant stakeholders, ensuring a comprehensive listing as follows:

(I)   **The 14 *who* questions of Stakeholder Identification**:
The following "systemic" questions will help to arrive at a suitable stakeholder (Table 5.1).

The power of this technique resides in its very simplicity. By seeking answers to these simple but essential questions, the project team will get to explore the "context" in order to identify stakeholders, their roles and responsibilities, and *locations* in keeping with the objectives and rationale of a specific project.

Again, a practical application illustration will assist in crystallising the technique; and bearing the "system" Concept of Operations (ConOps) in mind will get things on track from the outset.

Table 5.1 The 14 *who* questions of Stakeholder Identification, adapted from Hood[27]

1. Who pays for the system?	2. Who buys the system?
3. Who uses the system?	4. Who installs the system?
5. Who maintains the system?	6. Who delivers the system?
7. Who is against the system?	8. Who disposes of the system?
9. Who needs the system?	10. Who develops a competitor system?
11. Who specifies the system?	12. Who controls the system?
13. Who develops the system?	14. Other pertinent "systemic" questions?

Consider a project team just appointed to deliver a new mega shopping mall. Assuming the *Why* of the project is known (e.g., *to build the biggest shopping mall ever*), what questions should they ask in order to identify key stakeholders? By way of an example, Table 5.2 summarises a set of questions and answers.

The 17 italicised words under column [B] reflect the "identified" stakeholders. Those that are duplicated will get involved in multiple roles and responsibilities; furthermore, if the ConOps included *virtual shopping*, "3D-Technology Firms" would also pertain.

Table 5.2 Application of "the 14 *who* questions": an example

#	[A] The who question	[B] The team's response
01	*Who pays for the system?*	*Property Developers* to take loan from *banks*
02	*Who buys the system?*	*Property Management Firms* to take over the mall
03	*Who uses the system?*	*Shop Tenants* and *Office Tenants* will rent spaces
04	*Who installs the system?*	*Estates Agents* will sell and rent out floor spaces
05	*Who maintains the system?*	*Facilities Management Firms* to be appointed
06	*Who delivers the system?*	*Construction Companies* appointed on turnkey
07	*Who is against the system?*	*Small Shop Owners* and *Existing Malls* will resist
08	*Who disposes of the system?*	Ouch! Not determined at this Conceptual stage
09	*Who needs the system?*	*Shoppers, Shop Owners*, and *City Council* support
10	*Who develops a competitor system?*	*Chinese Consortium* planning a project close-by
11	*Who specifies the system?*	*Developers, Property Firms*, and *City Council* to do
12	*Who controls the system?*	*Property Firms* will manage as per *City Council*
13	*Who develops the system?*	Local *Architect, Engineering*, and *PM Firms* will do
14	*Who has similar system experience?*	*"Mall of Africa" Owner's Team* was very successful

Figure 5.1 Cartoon on the 14 *who* questions of Stakeholder Identification

(II) **The Stakeholder Wheel**:

This Stakeholder Identification technique has also gained popularity due to its simplicity – it guides teams by setting a few *generic* categories of stakeholders (Figure 5.2). These categories can be adapted as follows: Client, Client's Client, Management, User Groups, Investors, Government, Regulator, Tax Authorities, and Ombudsman.

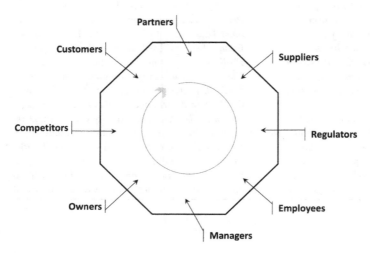

Figure 5.2 The Stakeholder Wheel, as per Shukla[54]

(III) **The Onion Diagram:**
Effective "leadership" would be needed to guide/support those entities (in dotted circle; Figure 5.3) affected by "new ways of working"; such stakeholders ought to be specifically identified!

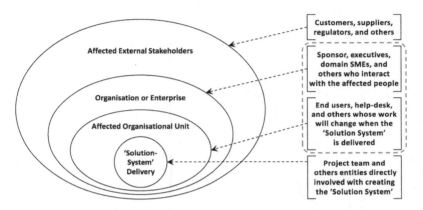

Figure 5.3 The Onion Diagram, adapted from Shukla[54]

(IV) **The Stakeholder Identification Matrix (SIM):**
The Stakeholder Identification tools and techniques discussed under sections (I), (II), and (III) are quite straightforward; they revolve around some form of categorisation, and thus, the identification process is linked to a *who* question – i.e., "Who could be found under so and so categories of stakeholders?"

Conversely, the Stakeholder Identification Matrix (SIM) combines categorisation with some form of "hierarchisation" of objectives that is project-context specific. Whereas this hierarchisation is left for the project team to determine based on the functions, processes, and/or outcomes of the "system", the categorisation axis includes prospective "agents" in the project ecology or Systems-of-interest. Table 5.3 provides a template for the application of the matrix.

In its practical application, SIM entails two separate steps: first, having defined the hierarchy, place an "X" in each of the boxes where "interactions" might be found; second, follow the reallocation rules, before *unpacking* the "Xs" into specific entities:

Table 5.3 The Stakeholder Identification Matrix (SIM), adapted from Renard[48]

Stake/Claim/Interest in Project §

Function(s), Process(es), or Output(s)/Come(s)#	Users, Customers	Beneficiaries	Suppliers	Influencers	Sponsors	Affected Parties	Right Holders	Legislators	Decision Makers	Project Workforce	⋯
$\varnothing_1$	×	×									
⋯		×									
$\varnothing_5$		×	×	×	×						
⋯			×	×	×			×	×	×	×
$\varnothing_9$		×		×		×	×	×	×		
⋯	×			×		×	×	×	×	×	×
$\varnothing_{13}$	×	×	×	×	×	×	×	×	×	×	×

Legend: #: As per Hierarchy of Objectives §: As per Project Context/Ecology

Rule (i) > If a particular column Ψ_i/row φ_j has an "x" in all boxes, the related Stakeholder$_i$/Area$_j$ will be parted into more detailed entities/areas – e.g., "Beneficiaries" column or row $\varnothing_{13}$

Rule (ii) > If there is no single "x" along any particular column Ψ_i/row φ_j then the related Stakeholder$_i$/Area$_j$ concerned is irrelevant and shall be discarded.

By way of illustration, the example below of a rail/road network project is discussed; the idea is to show that this technique is suitable for dealing with complexity in Large Infrastructure Projects, and thus, is able to identify stakeholders other tools could not.

The fictitious project is about building a 7000 km rail/road line between Lagos (Nigeria) and Mombasa (Kenya), thus running through Cameroon, Central African Republic, DR Congo, and Uganda. The line will join six countries with US$595 billion in total GDP, a 470 million population, and a GDP per capita ranging from US$385 to US$2400 per annum. It will also cross terrains of rainforests and deserts, and Christian and Muslim populations.

Apart from the usual role-players in the engineering and project management space, the project ecology is likely to interface several macroscopic "realms" such as suppliers, economic and finance, socio-political, ecological, rail and road technology industries, legal, and customer base, as well as logistics and commuter companies, travel and leisure agencies, toll-road companies, and individual users of diverse nationalities.

Considering the broad objectives of this project, the "functions/ processes/outcomes" of the envisaged systems could include the following: bulk and cargo transportation, commuter transit, tourism, planning, funding, feasibility studies, design, procurement, construction, operations, maintenance, disposal, political negotiations, commercial agreements, supply of electricity, supply of water, supply of diesel fuel, booking and ticketing, foreign exchange, immigration services, disease control, drug trafficking, regional integration, economic development, cultural exchanges, and social insecurity, just to name a few. The sheer length of the list attests to the complexity of the project.

In applying the SIM template, the project team (preferably in a workshop setting) will need to combine *perceptions* gained from the project background with insights from the project ecology (briefly discussed above) and the listed functions/processes/outcomes to determine "areas of interface" (i.e., boxes with "Xs", where an objective aspect applies in a specific realm of the project ecology). Thereafter, the two reallocation rules shall apply to possibly reconfigure the scenario (i.e., splitting or discarding columns and rows).

While completing this exercise could prove challenging, especially to the inexperienced, it is rather fulfilling in the end as, in this case, using the SIM technique will identify some "unsuspected" stakeholders. These could be drug cartels, local farmers, environmental protection agencies, banks (e.g., bureau de change), traders and hawkers, travel clinics, shop owners, global oil traders, tribal authorities, religious leaders, and armed militias. The alternative costs of failing to identify such stakeholders must not be underestimated!

6   Stakeholder Analysis

Stakeholder Analysis is the second step within the Four-Step SM Approach. The increasing realisation that proper attention to stakeholders is crucial to project success has led Stakeholder Analysis to becoming (more) important. The traditional, outdated way of undertaking such an analysis late in the "Execution" process in response to a crisis is unhealthy and counterproductive. It defeats the *proactive* essence of Systems Thinking.

Relevant stakeholders should be analysed for their current and future interests and bases of power in order to determine, in terms of their *input* and *buy-in*, the following:

(1) The key issues that need to be addressed (e.g., concerns, needs, expectations, rights and obligations, governance requirements, rapports of power, and roles and responsibilities);
(2) The degree to which each identified stakeholder could influence or be affected by the project's processes, activities, or outcomes (e.g., through an EIA process), as well as their strengths–weaknesses–opportunities–threats (i.e., SWOT Analysis);
(3) Relationships among various stakeholders and the impacts of such on outcomes;
(4) The broad *attitude* of key stakeholders – coalitions of support/opposition;
(5) The communication needs of main stakeholders – and input needed from them.

Stakeholder Analysis must be a focused and well-planned exercise aimed at answering questions that are directly relevant and useful to the planning and management process. This is in line with INCOSE's view: "A stakeholder is a party having a right, share or claim in a system or in its possession of characteristics that meet that party's needs and expectations".[25] Stakeholder Analysis should seek to determine such a right or claim.

Furthermore, PMBoK maintains:

> Stakeholder analysis is a technique of systematically gathering and analyzing quantitative and qualitative information to determine whose interests should be taken into account throughout the project. It identifies the interests, expectations, and influence of the stakeholders and relates them to the purpose of the project. It also helps to identify stakeholder relationships (with the project and with other stakeholders) that can be leveraged to build coalitions and potential partnerships to enhance the project's chance of success, along with stakeholder relationships that need to be influenced differently at different stages of the project or phase.[47]

One outcome of Stakeholder Analysis could consist of distinguishing between primary stakeholders (i.e., those that are directly involved) and secondary stakeholders (i.e., those that are peripheral to the delivery process), in addition to determining which stakeholders will probably support (not oppose) the project. This distinction is often needed to allow for a focused management of stakeholders, directing most efforts (i.e., prioritisation) where more interventions are required in terms of input and/or buy-in. In fact, "One of the biggest challenges in this [analysis] activity is the identification of the set of stakeholders from whom requirements [i.e., input] should be elicited".[25]

To overcome these challenges, an array of tools and techniques exist in the literature to assist in Stakeholder Analysis, and are based on combinations of the notions of power, interest, influence, or impact – such as the "Power versus Interest Grid" (Figure 6.1).

An insightful reading of this grid would suggest that stakeholders with both substantial power and high levels of interest in the project (or affected by it) are deemed "Players" (i.e., those the project team will need to prioritise and focus on in ensuing engagements); likewise, those stakeholders with little to no interest or power will fall under "Crowd". (Similar deliberations would arise from its variant, i.e., "Impact versus Influence Grid".)

Returning to the mega shopping mall example (Chapter 5) where 17 stakeholders were identified using the "14 *who* questions" framework, they are now classified as follows:

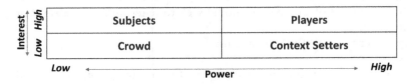

Figure 6.1 Power versus Interest Grid, as per Shukla[54]

(i)   *Crowd (Low Interest, Low Power)*

- Estates agents
- Facilities management firms
- (Other) existing malls

(ii) *Subjects (High Interest, Low Power)*

- Property firms
- (Prospective) office tenants
- Local architect firms
- Local engineering firms
- Local project management firms
- 3D-technology firms, *if virtual shopping*

(iii) *Context Setters (Low Interest, High Power)*

- (Prospective) shop tenants
- (Prospective) shoppers
- Small shop owners
- City council (i.e., planning bureau)

(iv) *Players (High Interest, High Power)* – who should be given the "highest" priority!

- Property developers
- Commercial banks
- Construction companies
- Chinese consortium

On face value, this classification grid suggests that the project team would be wise to prioritise their engagement efforts, *first*, on "Property developers", "Construction company" – and probably watch out for what the identified "Chinese consortium" plans might be, as they are planning a similar venture in close proximity. Although the "City council" and "Shoppers" have no direct interest in the project at this stage, their buy-in is still needed; further, crowds such as "Estates Agents" can be *energised* interest-wise to provide input.

A Stakeholder Analysis exercise largely culminates in an outcome that seeks to provide a "classification" of *generic* project stakeholders (and their attitude) as is shown in Table 6.1.

The Stakeholder Classification Table informs a different form of prioritisation in terms of roles and responsibilities the identified stakeholders could/should play in the project under consideration. For example,

Table 6.1 Stakeholder classification table, adapted from Shukla[54]

Stakeholder classification	
Champion	Will actively work for the success of the project
Supporter	In favour of the project but will probably not be very active in promoting it
Neutral	Has no expressed opinion either in favour or against the project
Critic	Not in favour of the project but probably not actively opposed to it
Opponent	Will work actively to disrupt, impede/sabotage, or derail the project
Blocker	Will just obstruct progress, maybe for reasons outside the project itself

"Property developers" should be allowed to perform as the *Champion* to actively work for the success of the project. However, the "City council" could turn into a *Blocker*, should the project fail to comply with by-laws.

Many Stakeholder Management practitioners argue as to which framework should be utilised for this Stakeholder Analysis exercise. So rather than approach this question from a standpoint of "either/or", it would be advisable to combine various tools and frameworks to benefit from their complementary perspectives and insights. This, again, is an important area where the project manager should provide "leadership".

Furthermore, Dr Bourne has recently submitted that "prior identification of mutuality" would expedite Stakeholder Analysis; this concept of *mutuality* is defined as follows:

(i)   How each stakeholder is important to the works/outcomes of the project;

(ii) What each stakeholder expects from project success/failure and its outcomes.

Stakeholder Analysis, thus, entails resolving either aspects of "Stakeholder Mutuality".

Both tasks are just as challenging *due to the dynamic nature of their outcomes over time*: "Australia's best-known building, the Sydney Opera House, was perceived as a 'white elephant' and an 'acoustic and aesthetic disaster' when it first opened in 1973. It is now regarded as the most recognisable tourist destination in Australia ... [not] as [a] failure".[11]

PMBoK[47] argues that to ensure comprehensive identification and listing (i.e., analysis) of stakeholders, "judgment and expertise should be sought from groups or individuals with specialized training or subject matter expertise". Such "judgment and expertise" could be gathered from senior management, other units within the organisation, identified key stakeholders, project managers (with similar experience), subject matter experts (SMEs) in the business or project area and industry groups, and consultants. Further, expert judgment can be obtained through individual consultations (one-on-one meetings, interviews, etc.) or through a panel format (focus groups, surveys, etc.), including professional and technical associations, guilds, regulatory bodies, and non-governmental organisations (NGOs).

Indeed, despite its apparent simplicity, an industry survey may provide an indication as to areas or aspects of the entity (i.e., project) management attention should focus on. For example:

> In a survey released ... by PriceWaterhouseCoopers (PWC) and the Economist Intelligence Unit (EIU), 34 percent of the 134 international bank respondents believed that reputation risk is the biggest risk to market and shareholder value faced by banks, while market and credit risk scored only 25 percent each.[16].

This survey makes it clear that the market and shareholders have more *interest* in "reputational risk".

Nevertheless, none of the above-mentioned Stakeholder Analysis tools and techniques seems to directly, explicitly satisfy a key requirement of Stakeholder Analysis, namely: "It also helps to identify stakeholder relationships (with the project and with other stakeholders) that can be leveraged to build coalitions and potential partnerships to enhance the project's chance of success". Not identifying the intersecting *relationships* within/across systems is a major deficiency in terms of the Systems Thinking approach. Accordingly, an example of an Occasional Friends and Foes diagram is introduced (see Figure 6.2).

The tools used so far in the analysis of the mega mall project are based on the "status" of the various stakeholders. From a Systems Thinking perspective, it is useful to also analyse the same stakeholders – a few more are added here to enrich the scenario – in terms of their relationships. The resultant "systemigram" is represented in see Figure 6.2.

The "linkages" such as the one between "City council" and the "Chinese consortium" (i.e., likely "opponents") that cross the "dividing line", from "Friends" to "Foes", are of utmost interest. For an opportunity is provided to fashion an engagement approach aimed, through such a linkage, at winning over a number of foes (i.e., project opponents). The ploy is to turn foes into friends (i.e., supporters), while consolidating "friends-of-friends". In large and "multilateral" projects, this Occasional Friends and Foes (OFF) Diagram would morph into a multi-layer diagram.

Relationships between or among role-players (i.e., stakeholders) in a project ecology are of the utmost importance to Stakeholder

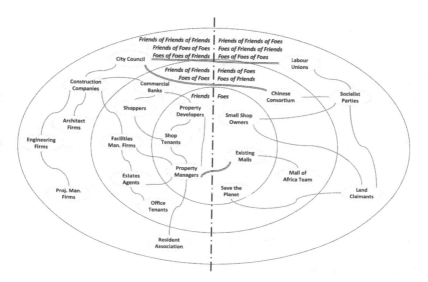

Figure 6.2 Occasional Friends and Foes (OFF) systemigram

Analysis – from a Systems Thinking perspective. This arises from the definition of a "system" as "A combination of interacting elements organized to achieve one or more stated purposes".[50] The operative words here are "interacting elements" (due to their relationships), without which this "combination" is reduced to a mere "grouping of things" that will not contribute to achieving a common purpose or set of objectives. Those relationships will differ in strength and in nature.

The OFF diagram used in the earlier example explores "relationships of affinity" (i.e., feeling of attraction, inclination to accommodate each other). Stakeholders could also display a set of relationships of a different nature, such as "relationships of influence" (*influence is the power exerted by an entity to affect and cause another one to change*). The next example depicts a situation where relationships across a "system-of-interest" are considered and discussed on the basis of their dominant (say, one-way) influence (Figure 6.3).

This diagram reveals a number of peculiar arrangements pertaining to relationships of influence in this project ecology. First, agents "L", "B", and "G" have no influence; agent "D" is the most *influential* (with six direct-outbound connections, plus two indirect ones), while agent "F" is the most *influenceable* (with five inbound connections). Hence, agent "D" will be used to *champion* the project, not agent "F" who will easily be swayed.

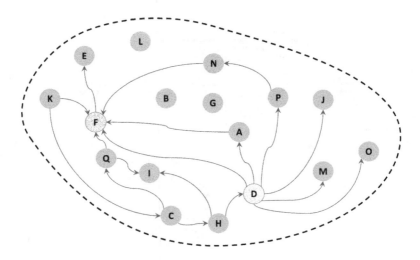

Figure 6.3 Example of a Lines of Influence Network (LOIN) systemigram

The foregoing discussions and examples will suffice, it is hoped, to dispel any doubt as to the merits of having "Analysis" as a stand-alone step, and as a feeder to "Strategy and Plan". For this crucial step is meant to

> analyze the potential impact or support each stakeholder could generate, and classify them so as to define an approach [i.e., engagement] strategy. In large stakeholder communities, it is important to prioritize the stakeholders to ensure the efficient use of effort to communicate [i.e., input] and manage their expectations [i.e. buy-in].[4]

Stakeholder Analysis tools (e.g., SWOT) could serve to "assess how key stakeholders are likely to react or respond to various situations, in order to plan how to influence them to enhance their support and mitigate potential negative impacts";[47] this suggestion certainly lends to outcomes of Stakeholder Analysis feeding into the Engagement Strategy.

7   Stakeholder Strategy and Plan

NETLIPSE insists that "Stakeholder Management should be a proactive and long-term priority; it is important that wide stakeholder support is achieved throughout the project to support the justification and need for its outputs".[43] Therefore, a deliberate strategy is required as to how the position, attitudes (i.e., how they might respond), and the relationships among stakeholders and with the project could be used to define an approach to securing relevant input and dependable buy-in on the part of stakeholders.

Alan Ferguson[20] has provided quite a simple definition of strategy as follows:

> "An approach or line to take to achieve a long-term aim". No wonder NETLIPSE argues, "Those projects which dealt with stakeholders on an ad hoc basis [or the *traditional* way] experienced far more problems with their stakeholders than those projects which developed a stakeholder [engagement] strategy early on in the project".[43]

As such, the project team may come up with a number of strategies, including branding. "Project Branding [i.e., image] can be a very effective way of reinforcing efforts to involve stakeholders as it gives the process a very clear identity"[43]; and for fostering alliances, "The project manager who neglects the building and maintenance of alliances with key political stakeholders will soon find indifference or opposition to his or her project".[14]

Still, it is advisable to start-off from the generic strategies available in the literature and expand to incorporate the sensitivities, intricacies, and vulnerabilities peculiar to the context of the project under consideration. Two templates are provided (Figures 7.1 and 7.2).

Figure 7.1 (Stakeholder Engagement Matrix) is based on a configuration of "Impact" and "Influence"); Figure 7.2 combines "Interest" with "Power".

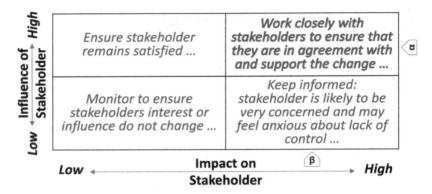

Figure 7.1 Stakeholder Engagement Matrix, as per IIBA[29]

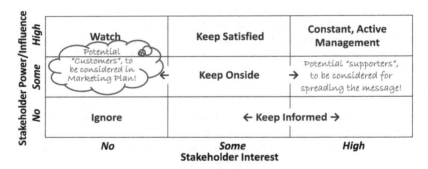

Figure 7.2 Stakeholder Interest–Influence Grid, adapted from Cadle and Years[45]

These templates provide a suitable (albeit generic) strategy for each cluster based on "Stakeholder Classification" preceding from the prior "Stakeholder Analysis" exercise. Consider, for instance, that any stakeholders scoring *high* on both the Interest and the Power/Influence scales would be approached on a "Constant, active management" basis. By the same token, the approach to engagement would be "Potential 'supporters', to be considered for spreading the message" for those stakeholders scoring respectively *High* and *Some* on the same scales; conversely, "Potential 'customers', to be considered in Marketing Plan" would apply as an approach to those scoring *No* and *Some* respectively.

Returning to the "Impact versus Influence Grid" (Figure 7.1) and the mega shopping mall scenario, stakeholders such as "Shoppers" (i.e., the very reason the mall will exist), "Shop tenants", and "Property developers" would be placed in the *High/High* quadrant. Therefore, the strategy towards them will be to "work closely with them to ensure that they are in agreement with and support the project". All the same, the project manager should "keep informed" stakeholders such as "Estates agents", "Office tenants", "Facilities management firms", and nearby "Small shop owners" who are falling in the *High/Low* quadrant – and who "may feel anxious about any (perceived) lack of control!"

It also transpires from the same grid that any stakeholders placed in the α-row should be *approached* in terms of "Buy-in", whereas those in the β-column should be for "Input". In case the ConOps also entailed *virtual shopping*, the Interest–Influence Grid could suggest that when suitable information (i.e., "input") is provided, "3D technology firms" would turn into "supporters, to be considered for promoting the mall online". The project manager will provide "leadership" in balancing input and buy-in expectations.

It shall have become clearer by now that an effective Stakeholder Analysis "workout" (see Chapter 5) will provide most of the information needed to devise an approach to Stakeholder Engagement for the enhancing of relationships and developing a plan for managing stakeholders. The Engagement Strategy follows the Y-Model, defining "who", "what", and "how" of "Stakeholder Engagement" – *who* (i.e., specific stakeholder), *what* (i.e., engagements required), and *how* (i.e., the way engagements shall be conducted).

A thorough Engagement Strategy seeks to define the intent, approach, or mode(s) of Stakeholder Engagement, as well as explicit message(s) that the project leadership needs to convey – *based on benefits/disbenefits to stakeholders* – and input(s) expected based on required commitment, degree of complexity, size, and stated goals of the project. The subsequent Engagement Plan (necessary for implementing strategy) will specify the activities, communication "packs", and impact measurement methods recommended.

This is the decisive step of the planning stage:

> The final [say, decisive?] step is to develop a strategy for how best to engage different stakeholders, how to "frame" or present the message or information so it is useful to them, and how to maintain a relationship with them – Identify the message, who will make each contact and how, and how to follow-up.[28]

It is common cause that effective execution of organisational strategies that carries the business from a current "alpha" status to a desirable, more competitive "beta" status will bring to most organisations the challenges of translating such strategies into project-like initiatives and of relying on proper and effective project management to deliver such projects successfully. The intended strategy will be realised as a result.[14]

Therefore, the Engagement Plan captures the crux of implementation steps as follows:

(1) Recommended engagement activities (i.e., their intent, scope, and dependencies);
(2) Major risks (i.e., threats and opportunities, to be managed via Risk Management);
(3) Monitoring and Control required (to measure and control engagement outcomes);
(4) Resources required (e.g., human resources, budget, timelines, documentation).

It then follows that Project Communication Planning should provide for effective communication among stakeholders at all required organisational levels throughout the project lifecycle (using channels such as verbal and telephone, printed media, meetings, audio-visual, intranet or internet, etc.) and is an essential part of Stakeholder Engagement – which it should complement and augment, but by no means supersede!

Adequate and robust implementation of the Engagement Plan will require a proper allocation of roles and responsibilities to prevent the kind of "cacophony" that arises when everybody is communicating with everybody else – the message gets confusing!

It was already submitted that the project team (both as a group and as each member in particular) will take care of identifying the relevant stakeholders, whereas the project manager (him/her alone) "should manage the influences of these various stakeholders in relation to the project requirements to ensure a successful outcome".[47]

However, in the practical implementation of the Engagement Plan (which addresses communication to and from at several levels within and across the project ecology), various members of the project team (not just the project manager) will be involved in this engagement activity or another. As a result, unless roles and responsibilities are clearly demarcated, chaos might soon ensue and the whole engagement will be in peril.

It thus becomes become essential to clarify who is actually 'Responsible' for a particular activity (e.g., communication, event, deliverable), and who shall be "Accountable", "Consulted", or merely "Informed" about the execution and/or outcomes of any tasks. Accordingly, the RACI Matrix could be utilised to capture allocation of "engagement" roles, addressing crucial aspects of *leadership* and *mode* (e.g., centralised versus spread). The Stakeholder Engagement Plan, and its RACI Matrix, should be *incorporated* into the Project Execution Plan (PEP), and "treated in same way as other 'core' project activities!"

Table 7.1 Example of a RACI Matrix for a Stakeholder Engagement Plan

	Stakeholder 1 • • •		*Stakeholder 5* • • •		*Stakeholder 9*
Engagement activity/ deliverable 1	R	A	1	1	C
• • •	C	C	C	C	R
Engagement activity/ deliverable 5	1	1	A	R	C
• • •	1	1	1	A	R
Engagement activity/ deliverable 9	C	C	C	A	R

Note: R = Responsible; A = Accountable; C = Consulted; 1 = Informed.

There are simple, but practical "rules" to the application of this RACI Matrix, including:

(1) No activity shall be without an accountable and responsible person allocated to it;
(2) Responsibility for an activity could be delegated, but its accountability should not;
(3) Two entities should not be responsible for the same activity, at the same time; but the same entity can be responsible for several activities, if capacity will allow them.

Table 7.2 provides an outline of the "Stakeholder Engagement Strategy and Plan", which should, at a minimum, address the following engagement aspects/components as reflected in this table.

It shall become apparent from the content of this table that, even as PMBoK argues that Stakeholder Management is all about Engagement Strategy and its related Plan:

Stakeholder management is more than improving communications and requires more than managing a team. Stakeholder management

Table 7.2 Synopsis of the Stakeholder Engagement Strategy and Plan

Stakeholder Engagement Strategy	The Strategy is a compilation of information analysed as follows:
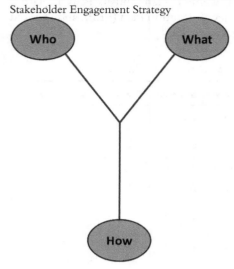	• *Stakeholder names, designations*; • Key interests and issues; • *Relationships with stakeholders and possible impacts on outcomes*; • Current status (e.g., advocate, supporter, neutral, critic, blocker); • *Current vs. Desired Support and Receptiveness – Change of attitude*; • Desired project roles (if any) and ways to exploit stakeholders' relationships; • *Message, Platforms, and Input(s)* needed (i.e., to/from stakeholders); • Proposed Engagement Roles (e.g., championing, endorsement); • *Interventions required* (e.g., acts of goodwill, contributions to welfare); • Engagement Approaches (e.g., direct vs. facilitated, persuasive vs. tactful).
Stakeholder Engagement Plan	• The Plan captures the essence of implementation steps as follows: • *Recommended Engagement Initiatives* (e.g., intent, scope, sequencing); • *Communications Events* (e.g., PR to convey message; input and validation); • *Resources Required* (e.g., human resources, skills, budget, timeframes); • *Key Risks, Assumptions,* as well as *Monitoring* and *Control* required.

Table 7.3 Example of a Stakeholder Engagement Strategy and Plan

The Strategy	*Stakeholder name and designation*
	Property developers
	Key interest and issues
	They are champions of the mega shopping mall project and will fund it through loans
	Relationships with other stakeholder and impacts on outcomes
	They will work closely with property management firms to operationalise the mall
	Current status
	As the initiators of the project, property developers will indeed champion the project
	Change of attitude desired
	Their patronage of the project is secured; yet, they should embrace new technologies, e.g., virtual shopping
	Desired project roles (if any)
	It will be advisable to include their representative in the project steering committee
	Message, platform, and input needed
	They would provide input as to "design requirements", as well as industry knowledge
	Proposed project/partnership roles
	In championing the project, they would promote the mall vis-à-vis financial institutions and the construction industry
	Intervention required
	Their sponsorship to be recognised by inviting them to name the envisaged mega mall
	Engagement approaches
	Owing to their vested interests in the project, they would be engaged directly, openly
The Plan	*Recommended engagement initiatives*
	Monthly steering committee to be attended by property developers
	Communication events
	They are to be invited in validating and approving project deliverables and outcomes
	Resources required
	No additional resources will be required in engaging property developers
	Key risks, assumptions, and monitoring required
	Their support is secured, but reluctance to embrace new technologies is problematic

Note: individual strategies and plans will be aggregated at project/programme levels!

is about creation and maintenance of relationships between the project team and stakeholders, with the aim to satisfy their respective needs and requirements within project boundaries.[47]

− The Strategy!

This process generates the stakeholder management plan, which contains detailed plans on how effective stakeholder management can be realized. As the project progresses, the membership of the stakeholder community and required level of engagement may change, therefore, stakeholder management planning is an iterative process that is reviewed on a regular basis by the project manager.[47]

− Its related Plan!

The centrality of Stakeholder Management to project delivery shall not be understated:

Stakeholder Management activities should be managed at the same level of definition and with the same diligence as the above-mentioned processes − or any other activities as required by the project lifecycle methodology. Any form of asymmetry between SM processes and other activities will prove fatal.

Yes, it will prove fatal to the whole project.

Furthermore, the PMBoK sounds a warning to project managers regarding how they should handle sensitivities around the information contained in the Strategy and Plan.

Project managers should be aware of the sensitive nature of the stakeholder management plan and take appropriate precautions. For example, information on stakeholders who are resistant to the project can be potentially damaging, and due consideration should be given regarding the distribution of such information. When updating the stakeholder management plan, the validity of underlying assumptions should be reviewed to ensure continued accuracy and relevancy.[47]

Again, reverting to the mega shopping mall situation, "Property developers" are discussed (see Table 7.3) in terms of the Strategy and Plan "to satisfy their respective needs and requirements".

8 Stakeholder Engagement

Everything discussed thus far has been aimed at introducing the concept and importance of Stakeholder Management, and at setting the scene for its most important part, namely, Stakeholder Engagement. "Stakeholders should be seen as very important by project delivery entities, not least because of the adverse impact that stakeholders can have on the timescales for achieving the consents and approvals for work to commence".[1, 67]

Stakeholders ought to be approached, engaged, and communicated to with great care!

The strategies and plans previously developed, as well as the insights gleaned during the foregoing and crucial steps of the proposed Stakeholder Management approach, should now be put into effect when "the rubber hits the road" in actual engagements. "Sustaining the relationships and measuring the effectiveness of communication [i.e., engagements] with stakeholders can yield strong benefits for a disproportionately low amount of time and expenditure".[43] Hostilities can also escalate disproportionately! Someone has advised:

> Stakeholder Engagement is critical to the success of every project in every organisation I have worked with. By engaging the right people in the right way in your project, you can make a big difference to its success ... and to your career.[63]

Therefore:

> Stakeholder Engagement is the process of communicating and working with stakeholders to meet their needs/expectations, address issues as they occur, and foster appropriate stakeholder engagement in project activities throughout the project life cycle. The key benefit of this process is that it allows the project manager to increase support and reduce resistance from stakeholders [towards the attainment of

the ConOPs], significantly increasing the chances to achieve project success.[47]

PMBoK[47] argues:

> Managing stakeholder engagement helps to increase the probability of project success by ensuring that stakeholders clearly understand the project goals, objectives, benefits, and risks. This enables them to be active supporters of the project and to help guide activities and project decisions. By anticipating people's reactions to the project, proactive actions can be taken to win support or minimize negative impacts.

Relevant stakeholders as identified (and duly analysed) at the preceding stages now need to be "continuously" engaged, involved, and communicated to as per the devised Stakeholder Strategy and Plan. This is the most appropriate time when the *dynamic* aspects (arising from Systems Thinking) of Stakeholder Management will really unfold:

(1) First, appropriate care ought to be taken in implementing the Stakeholder Plan;
(2) Second, "responses" (including from newly identified stakeholders) to both engagement activities and other project processes (as well as their outcomes) are to be closely and carefully monitored – i.e., issues and risks are duly recorded;
(3) Last, feedback into the initial Strategy and Plan for review and constant updating should take place – and herein lies the shifting point between success and failure or disaster, as far as robust Stakeholder Management is concerned.

Further, "The current engagement level of all stakeholders needs to be compared to the planned engagement levels required for successful project completion. Stakeholder engagement throughout the life cycle of the project is critical to project success".[47]

To this end, and having made accommodation of elicitation of input and elucidation of communication to stakeholders, "Stakeholder Engagement" includes activities such as:

(a) Engaging stakeholders at appropriate project stages to obtain or confirm their input and buy-in, and their continued commitment to the success of the project;
(b) Clarifying and resolving issues (i.e., risks having already occurred) that are raised;

(c) Addressing potential concerns that have not yet become issues and anticipating future problems that may be raised by stakeholders. Such concerns need to be identified and discussed as soon as possible to assess associated project risks;

(d) Managing stakeholder expectations through negotiation and communication, and resolving conflicts as they arise in order to ensure project goals are achieved.

The above theoretical considerations and principles will need to be put into practice. It is all about consultations, negotiations, resolution of grievances, partnerships, and good gestures. Practical wisdom will come through years of experience on the ground.

For instance, a senior construction manager of a local firm commended the project management team he has been working with for their "upfront engagement with the community". Mr John K has never faced angry stakeholders on any of his sites for the past 20 years; he gratefully added, "I have also witnessed a noticeable increase in availability of casual labour every time a good gesture [e.g., in-kind donation] was made towards the community". One ignores such great wisdom at his/her own peril!

Regrettably, many (if not most) project managers still reduce Stakeholder Engagement down to a simplistic, optional add-on, and largely one-way "communication exercise".

Nevertheless, experience in Large Infrastructure Projects (LIPs) has confirmed that adequate, timely, and effective consultation and engagement with key stakeholders is of paramount importance in project planning, development, execution, and operation. NETLIPSE[43] described "Stakeholder Engagement" across 15 LIPs in Europe:

- "The objectives of engagement with stakeholders have been to obtain involvement and then to enter into a constructive dialogue. Much of the information [i.e. input] available to these external organisations is of potential value if it can be captured at an appropriate stage of the project" – such a dialogue may be required by legislation!

- "There was a dedicated part of the project team responsible for stakeholder relationships. An overall communications plan – which had been drawn up in line with BAE's stated commitment to consistent, transparent, proactive and open engagement – governed relationships with external parties involved in the project".

- "Previous infrastructure projects, in particular the by-passing of Innsbruck, were planned and executed by ÖBB 'in distant Vienna'. Local stakeholders had not been involved and the scheme's implementation was greeted with considerable hostility. This hostility initially spilt over into the early stages of the Unterinntalbahn project. The Tyrolean provincial assembly ruled that 'not a metre of over-ground track will be built in Tyrol'. By 2005 an independent opinion poll established that only 7% of respondents viewed the project unfavourably. This turn-round was achieved by a carefully planned and executed strategy of engagement. Groups of local communes were brought together with consultant engineers and specialists to develop proposals for the routing and features ultimately agreed upon".

The NETLIPSE Report presented general principles gathered from practical examples. Many project practitioners have shared nuggets of wisdom based on their experience:

- "Failure to attend to the [1]information and [2]concerns of stakeholders clearly is a kind of flaw in thinking or action that too often and too predictably leads to poor performance, outright failure or even disaster", Prof J.M. Bryson echoes Tuchman.
- Thompson who introduces herself as "experienced project manager" (with 15-year of experience as a change consultant) said about Stakeholder Engagement: "Even when it is not all good news, it is usually a good idea to manage stakeholders' expectations about likely problems as early as possible. This gives all parties involved time to think through how to manage such issues on their part, and therefore preserves one's reputation for reliability".[63] She knows what she is talking about!
- "Get introduced, build good rapport and relationships with your stakeholders; send greetings, gifts on festivals, pamper them within acceptable ethical and corporate norms – This is a good way to remain connected",[54] recommends Vijay S. Shukla.

It transpires from this body of advice that Stakeholder Engagement is by no means a straight-forward, systematic process; it blends "methodical" and "expressive" aspects. The expressive, artistic part entails maintaining "thrust" (i.e., commitment to project objectives), building "trust" (i.e., from each bona-fide stakeholder), and gathering "learnings" (i.e., of changing patterns of behaviour in the network of stakeholders)[17] – it goes as far as watching your own body language and avoiding lies/misrepresentations.

Finally, one ought to realise that this engagement exercise should not concern itself *exclusively* with those stakeholders outside the confines of

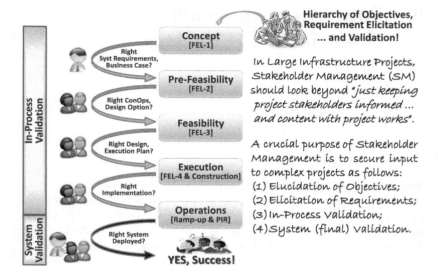

Figure 8.1 Stakeholder Engagement and the V&V Process, as per Ryen[50]

the project team. Relevant stakeholders, identified as those from whom requirements should be elicited, ought to be engaged (including internally) in terms of Verification and Validation (V&V) (Figure 8.1).

Stakeholder Engagement supports V&V, which plays a crucial role in assuring the project delivers a "system" that will conform to owner/customer requirements (e.g., real needs). In fact, Stakeholder Management also relates to Risk Management and other processes.

9 Four-Step Approach and Generic PM Processes

When dispelling the myth that Stakeholder Management (SM) is somewhat of an "off-line" exercise, or something that is not (should not be) part of core project delivery, a point was made that because of such a myth, "the project itself could be at risk!" SM is *intrinsically* linked to Risk Management (RM) – e.g., RM processes (e.g., mitigation of risks) involve stakeholders and flawed SM entails vulnerabilities (i.e., risks) to projects.

This position, as a key principle underpinning the *Four-Step Stakeholder Management Approach*, entails the proposed steps dovetailing with and aligning to any other Project Management Process as defined in the PMBoK. This includes 47 PM Processes that are logically grouped and categorised into five Process Groups:[47] (1) Initiating; (2) Planning; (3) Executing; (4) Monitoring and Controlling; and (5) Closing.

Furthermore, superposing the proposed Four-Step SM Approach to these process groups may make it appear (wrongly so, though) that the four steps fall short of two crucial processes; explicitly, the "Monitoring and Control" and the "Closing" Process Groups.

The reality is that "Stakeholder Management activities should be managed at the same level of definition and with the same diligence as any other activities required by the project lifecycle methodology". This is best achieved by not only aligning SM activities to "Initiating", "Planning", and "Executing" processes, but more so by incorporating them into the same (i.e., not separate) "Monitoring and Control" and "Closing" processes.

Figure 9.1 seeks to map out the Four-Step SM Approach and align each particular step to specific Process Groups. It also shows how "Monitoring and Control" as well as "Closing" processes support the proposed approach, including how "Lessons Learned" arising from SM activities are incorporated into the overall project delivery process.

From a process-group perspective, it is thus established that the four components pertaining to Stakeholder Management (Identification,

Figure 9.1 "Four-Step Approach to SM", mapped against PM Processes

Analysis, Strategy and Plan, and Engagement) will indeed dovetail into *generic* project management processes. As projects are separated into distinct lifecycle phases/subcomponents, e.g., Concept Development, Feasibility Study, Design, Prototype, Build, or Test, most PM and SM processes can be repeated for each lifecycle phase/subcomponent, as applicable:

(1) *Initiating*: Stakeholder Identification shall take place at this early stage, NOT at the tail-end of planning to *hard-sell* the project to some difficult stakeholders;

(2) *Planning*: Stakeholder Analysis should be incorporated at this stage. This input (e.g., needs, expectations of stakeholders) is most valuable for Project Scope Definition. Further, its outcome informs the development of an effective Stakeholder Strategy and Plan, and the subsequent engagement activities will be devised and planned at the same level of definition as any other project task or work-package, bringing SM into the main activities, as "core" to project delivery;

(3) *Executing*: Stakeholder Engagement activities should be carried out with the same diligence as any other Project Execution activity, with stakeholders being involved in decision making (e.g., major change options and risks discussed with key stakeholders in proven engagement-platforms before being implemented);

(4) *Monitoring and Controlling*: SM performance is tracked and reviewed in terms of:
   (i) Stakeholders' input and responses to "engagement" activities/ artefacts;
   (ii) Stakeholders' expectations and responses to other PM "work-packages";
   (iii) Outcomes of both items (i) and (ii) are reviewed and analysed to update the "Stakeholder Strategy and Plan" – with "feedback" to stakeholders;

(5) *Closing*: engagement activities are closed-out in a controlled manner, ensuring all accountabilities are discharged or handed over to operations – and Lessons Learned are gathered and finalised for due inclusion in future (similar) projects.

However, only in small projects will the above five Process Groups apply in a *single-run* manner. They normally repeat themselves in cycles, largely known as the project lifecycle. Accordingly, ISO 15288:2008 states:

> A lifecycle model that is composed of stages shall be established. The life cycle model comprises one or more stage models, as needed. It is assembled as a sequence of stages that may overlap and/or iterate, as appropriate for the scope, magnitude, and complexity, changing needs [or context] and opportunities.[32]

Such a project lifecycle is the "racetrack" of project delivery efforts.[34]

Moreover, stakeholders would have varying levels of responsibility and authority when participating in large and complex projects. These might change over the course of the project lifecycle – Stakeholder Management should, thus, align to the project lifecycle!

> "The phases [of such project lifecycle] are generally sequential, and their names and numbers are determined by the management and control needs of the organization or organizations involved in the project [i.e. stakeholders], the nature of the project itself, and its area of application … phases can be broken down by functional or partial [project] objectives, intermediate results or deliverables, specific milestones within the overall scope of work, or financial availability."[33, 38, 44]

The project lifecycle governs the SM process! (See Figure 9.2.)

Although Execution consumes the bulk of delivery efforts, SM will apply to all the phases.

> A well-documented project lifecycle model enables us to apply Systems Thinking to creating, planning, scheduling, and managing the project [stakeholders] through all of its phases, and to evaluating both the success and the value of both the project and results that the project has produced. This is of greatest benefit to the project owner, key stakeholders, the ultimate user of the project results, and the social beneficiaries of those results – whether it is a new process plant, a highway … or a new product.[5]

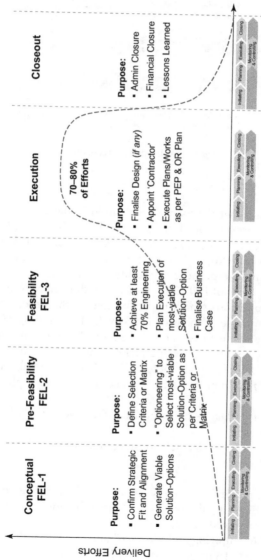

Figure 9.2 Generic Project Lifecycle, mapped against PM Processes

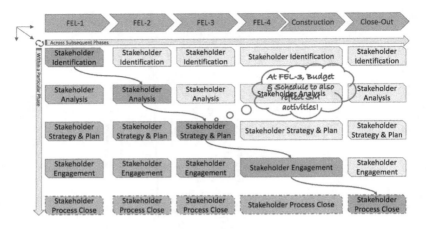

Figure 9.3 Stakeholder Management Processes, mapped over the generic Project Lifecycle

This stance entails that the focus of Stakeholder Management, as well as the approach to Stakeholder Engagement, should be defined in keeping with specific phases of the lifecycle. Figure 9.3 maps out key SM processes along a *generic* Project Lifecycle, with the focus for a particular SM step aligning with the purpose of the lifecycle phase, e.g., "Stakeholder Analysis" is the focus of FEL-2 to coincide with project "optioneering".

This figure points to which particular step of the process SM should focus on at each phase of the project lifecycle. By mapping SM activities along two perpendicular axes, i.e., "longitudinal – across lifecycle phases" and "latitudinal – within a specific phase", the figure implies that while "Identification" should be the focus of FEL-1 (Conceptual), two vantage points (which are complementary, of necessity) should apply as follows:

(i) *Longitudinal looking* – high-level considerations to "Identification" across phases;
(ii) *Latitudinal looking* – detailed considerations of the other steps, within the FEL-1 phase.

The same will, respectively, apply to "Analysis" at FEL-2 and "Strategy and Plan" at FEL-3; while steps (e.g., "Identification") covered in prior phases will be reviewed for relevancy.

However, "Monitoring and Control" and "Close-out" will combine SM activities (e.g., EIA mitigations) and PM lifecycle activities throughout the project lifecycle. Therefore, the "Monitoring and Control" and "feedback" processes will expand beyond the completion of the physical deliverables to assure the results of SM remain beneficial in Operations. For the sake of transparency, key stakeholders and external monitors may be involved.

Nonetheless, stakeholders will be informed of project completion (or termination) and their respective responses, together with any proposed follow-up actions on engagement activities, should be analysed and duly documented to inform the Post-Implementation Reviews (PIRs), and for inclusion into the Lessons-Learned dossiers. To that end, the project manager, again, will provide the right "leadership" to the team.

10 Advanced topics in Stakeholder Management

As stated in previous chapters, "stake" is the operative word in stakeholder; and when the stakes are high (as often in Large Infrastructure Projects, LIPs) conflicts are likely to arise — and to persist. The project team must be equipped to understand their nature and suitable remedies.

This chapter, thus, introduces the central notions of (1) Team Dynamics (from a Systems Thinking perspective), (2) Stakeholder Salience, and (3) the Triple Bottom-Line, and (4) discussions on "How to remedy an SM Process that has gone wrong" will follow. Putting the above in practice, again, entails a good measure of "leadership" — as noted in Chapter 4.

10.1 The notion of team dynamics in large and complex project organisations

Glass et al.[22] argue that the Realisation System (i.e., LIP project team), just as the LIP Solution System itself, is actually a Complex Adaptive System (i.e., consists of a large number of mutually interacting and interwoven parts and agents). This makes it a Complex-Adaptive-System-of-Systems (CASoS) with three features:

(i) An emergent structure that is complex (i.e., it being a network of networks);
(ii) An emergent behaviour (i.e., grow and adapt, contain people) that is complex;
(iii) Have parts and agents that are interdependent.

The project delivery team for LIPs is, thus, a CASoS; hence, the Project Team forms the "core" of a Complex Adaptive System.

As such, "relationships" between and among members of the Project Team are more important (to the team system) than the strengths of individual members — any soccer or rugby coach will tell you that!

The following "dynamics" (adapted from Dr D. Rotach, "Systems and Conflict"[49]) will affect the strength and/or nature of relationships among the team members:

(1) ANXIETY, which arises from *unresolved* issues within or around the team and is intensified whenever a crisis emerges and managed (or mismanaged) depending on level of maturity of leaders in the team system. When people choose "reactive" over rational behaviours, team functioning will be impaired;

(2) HOMEOSTASIS manifests itself when the team system fights to *obstinately* preserve the "status quo", whether unwittingly or in seeking some benefits;

(3) IDENTIFIED PATIENT applies whenever an individual or an issue is arbitrarily *selected* to carry the blame or be used as the scapegoat for project mishaps;

(4) INFORMAL CHIEF is a person without any official title or authority, but who still has a strong influence and/or a "leverage" over a team system. He/she is able to sway opinions or steer discussions and, thus, the team behaviours;

(5) EMOTIONAL TRIANGLE occurs whenever two individuals facing *discomfort* will involve − *triangle-in* − a third one − each one trying to enlist their support. Whenever leaders in a team system *triangle* with others, a higher anxiety ensues;

(6) EMOTIONAL MATURITY refers to the capacity to define and abide by one's own life goals or values in the midst of anxiety or pressure to conform to the team. This may create a difficulty for the leader who might end up *herding* donkeys;

(7) UNSPOKEN RULES are those *guidelines* (i.e., how things should be done and are often prejudice-based) that are understood by most people to apply but do not exist in a written form. Most "unhealthy" team systems deny that such rules exist until they are broken − and punishment or retaliation is called for.

The above "Seven Dynamics of Team-Systems" that are applicable to LIPs might not be as exhaustive as one would have wished, but they should suffice in alerting the project manager, lest he/she "sleepwalks into a terrain strewn with land mines".

For instance, the prudent project manager would want to avoid the "triangle-in" of a faction of the project team, lest he/she contributes to heightening anxiety. Likewise, the project manager should also seek to establish and duly publish any "rules" that team members ought to abide by; and treat issues and challenges in an objective and factual manner so that no unfortunate person is blamed unjustly.

The dynamic nature of a project team as a CASoS causes some otherwise *minor* "human dynamics" within the team system to trigger *unintended* behaviours in other areas, with *major* negative consequences.

Not only are team members closely (and in multiple ways) interconnected to one another, but the aforesaid Seven Dynamics also connect, leading to one another. For instance, some *unworthy* fellow could ascend to "Informal Chieftaincy" by craftily playing "Emotional Triangulation" and setting up people as "Identified Patients". Thus, especially when operating in bad faith or seeking some nefarious agendas, such "Informal Chiefs" protect the status quo and use "Unspoken Rules" to punish those they might perceive as enemies. In the process, they leave behind a trail of unsuspected "Anxiety"; they often trigger a "domino effect"!

10.2 The notion of Stakeholder Salience

Stakeholder Salience, as recently applied to project management, indicates the degree to which project managers give priority to competing stakeholders' claims. It is a function of their possession of one or more of the following three attributes:[9]

(i)   POWER is the "ability" of agents to exercise their will despite a likely resistance. In the context of stakeholders, the concept of AGENCY will be more appropriate; it is construed as the "capacity" and willingness to take action, to exert POWER.

(ii) LEGITIMACY is a generalised perception or assumption that the actions of an entity are desirable, proper, or appropriate within some socially constructed systems of norms, values, beliefs, and definitions; it is about *"the right to act"*.

(iii) URGENCY is the degree to which stakeholder claims need *immediate* attention.

Given the increasing demands stakeholders are placing on projects nowadays, project managers are being confronted with the challenge of satisfying a much *broader* base of differing stakeholder's expectations with scarce resources. This difficulty is further exacerbated by the requirement for (and as a consequence of) a more inclusive notion of stakeholder – as discussed under Section 10.3.

Therefore, successful Stakeholder Management should rely upon the accurate measurement of Stakeholder Salience in order to correctly prioritise competing stakeholders' claims. Indeed, along the lines of the essential, yet contentious, question of *whom* and *what* matters in projects, the notion of "salience" adds a new dimension to stakeholder analysis as it allows project managers (and other project participants) to effectively prioritise the needs, expectations, or demands stakeholders place on projects, which would require managerial attention.

However, how does one begin to gauge "Salience"? Taking a cue from a research paper presented by Bell,[9] a theoretical Salience model is proposed in Figure 10.1.

In keeping with this model, Stakeholder Salience is represented by the area captured by any given combination of Power, Legitimacy, and Urgency scales. Salience of entities "X", "Y", and "Z" will be concurrently interpreted as follows:

- Entity "X" has great power but no legitimacy, and a relatively high urgency; its Salience is represented by the area between point X, the "Urgency", and the "Power/Legitimacy" axes. This specific stakeholder carries a fairly high Salience (i.e., Immoral Claim) and shall therefore receive a "pushback", "ward-off" type of attention (e.g., political sabotage is a real threat from such a stakeholder).
- Entity "Y" has Power and Legitimacy, with a fairly high Urgency. This particular stakeholder carries a high Salience (i.e., Authority) and he/she therefore receives a "pull" attention from management, provided it is compliance-based.
- Entity "Z", on the contrary, has little to no Power; its Legitimacy combined with a somewhat low Urgency has resulted in a low

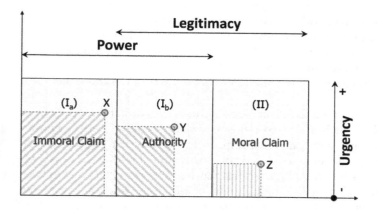

Figure 10.1 Stakeholder Salience (i.e., Patterned Area), as per Bell et al.[9]

Salience (i.e., Moral Claim); he/she should receive a rather limited "pull in" attention that is ethics-based.

The project manager shall also appreciate that even if entity "X", as a stakeholder, might emerge with a higher Salience (and probably some bullying too), entity "Y" is actually the one to satisfy the most (i.e., prioritising their claims) as it carries (more) authority – reversing this order of priority could prove counterproductive.

10.3 The notion of the "Triple Bottom–Line"

Value creation is generally believed to be the primary reason for the existence of any business enterprise – and the notion of value is traditionally viewed narrowly as financial value for shareholders. Project initiatives, which are seen as building blocks to strategy implementation, are often measured with the same yardstick – phrases such as "to maximise the NPV of projects" still dominate conversations.

This stance should no longer be tolerated given today's environmentally conscious paradigm; hence, the yardstick has to evolve into a notion of value that is expressed in terms of the Triple Bottom-Line, namely: economic, social, and environmental performance. Yet there is a rising *populism* that thrives on denying this complexity!

Nevertheless, King IV compels the "governing body" to assume responsibility for the governance of stakeholder relationships – to set the direction and to approve policy that articulates and gives effect to "how such relationships should be approached", e.g., that projects will seek "returns for all stakeholders", not just for shareholders.

While project initiators/sponsors and funders deserve returns on their investment, many other stakeholders (e.g., the neighbouring communities) might have given up something (e.g., source of fresh water) or had to suffer (e.g., noise/dust pollution) for the sake of the project. Thus, their expectations of "returns" are also legitimate.

Further, citing UK government sources, Slack[55] remarked that:

> CSR is the business contribution to our sustainable development goals … it is about how business takes account of its economic, social and environmental impacts in the way it operates – maximizing the benefits and minimizing the downsides … we see CSR as the voluntary actions that business [or projects] can take, over and above compliance with minimum legal requirements, to address both its own competitive interests and the interests of wider society.

It would be a classic case of the "Tragedy of the Commons" if "Every user [e.g., projects] benefits directly from its [shared resources] use, but shares the costs of its abuse [i.e., rising pollution] with everyone else".[38]

The company being so integral to the society within which it operates, the corporation is expected to be (and be seen to be) a decent citizen. This involves social, environmental, and definitely economic issues – the "Triple Bottom-Line". Consequently, on top of the traditional financial returns (economic performance), projects, in addition, need to satisfy (and be seen as value-adding to) their stakeholders in terms of social and environmental performance. In fact, Taylor[61] (in 1971) predicted that the importance of shareholders will diminish and that, in the 1970s or beyond, business (and projects) would be managed for the benefit of their stakeholders as well.

Moreover, the Constitution of South Africa (Section 24, Bill of Rights) stipulates that "Everyone has the right (a) to an environment that is not harmful to their health or well-being; and (b) to have the environment protected, for the benefit of present and future generations, through reasonable legislative and other measures". From this point of view, virtually every citizen could be a legitimate stakeholder.

The last thing any smart project manager needs is a confrontation with "green" activists – many infrastructure projects have suffered setbacks on this account. Even in Africa, environmentalist lobby groups are becoming a stronger (than ever) force to be reckoned with as stakeholders, namely in Large Infrastructure Projects.

The common excuse that applying the Triple Bottom-Line approach to determining the viability of a large and complex project would make it expensive and thus not feasible is absurd; who can tell of "the costs of pollution to future generations"?

10.4 How to remedy an SM Process that has gone wrong

The more project practitioners (particularly those involved in LIP delivery) will embrace and practice Stakeholder Management, even growing mature in its practical application, the more the industry will come across incidences of failed Stakeholder Management in project instances – if they have not already done so!

The right approach to remedying such situations would be to *right away* enforce the Four-Step Approach to SM by reverting to "Stakeholder Identification" (Step 1) and then proceeding to catch up the pertinent component, namely Steps 2, 3, or 4. (This is definitely not a case of, "If it does not work, do it again!", as it may sound!)

First.   Identify all stakeholders *at that point in time*, and then proceed as suited;

Second.   Analyse their needs, powers, interests, and "positions" vis-à-vis the project;

Third.   Develop the pertinent Strategy and Plan for engaging and involving relevant stakeholders *under the given circumstances* – including "Conflict Resolution";

Fourth.   Implement that Strategy and Plan (i.e., engagement activities/ deliverables) with the same diligence and expediency as any other "core" project activity.

Stakeholder Management seeks to achieve "well-orchestrated engagements" with a range of project stakeholders in order to secure the relevant input and dependable buy-in, which are *concomitantly* important to the project success – treating it any differently is a recipe for disaster or an open invitation to failure!

> Don't you wait until the Project Steering Committee meeting descends into a brawl before you consider applying Stakeholder Management!

As the project team move in their eagerness to complete the project, they may step on "edgy, but influential toes" in some factions of stakeholders. Once the Stakeholder Management process has failed, it is only a matter of time before the project also fails.

The Johannesburg Bus Rapid Transfer (BRT) programme known as "Rea Vaya" (We are moving) was designed to rationalise and improve public transport systems on the eve of the 2010 Soccer World Cup. But it was put "on hold" just four weeks before the start of the Confederation Cup (June 2009), citing a lack of cooperation on the part of taxi operators (who then retorted, "We were not consulted ... they don't listen to us – it won't happen!"). Thankfully, they somehow relented before the World Cup proper.

In the "Horn of Africa", a dam project[31] *nearly* took a turn for the worst: threats of war! The US\$4 billion Grand Ethiopian Renaissance Dam is set to be the biggest hydropower plant in Africa – and is hailed as a national achievement, "as big as Aswan High Dam in Egypt was in the 1960s"; but Egypt would not take kindly to such an *insensitive* comparison. Since Ethiopia announced plans nearly a decade ago to build a massive hydroelectric dam along the Blue Nile tributary, the Egyptian government has waited in dread at the catastrophic prospects that its Nile freshwater lifeline could slow by as much as 25%.

"We don't have any other resource in Egypt except the Nile water" warned Professor Nader Nour el-Din (soil and water expert at Cairo University) – "This will harm Egypt!"[31]

Alternately threatening and negotiating, Egyptian officials have sought to scuttle or minimise the impact of the planned 6450-megawatt facility, with Ethiopia planning to fill it in three years and Egypt asking for 15 years to better prepare for the future. Since the Nile runs the length of the country from its southern border with Sudan north into the Mediterranean Sea, the "sacred" river provides more than 90% of Egypt's fresh water.

In 2013, Egypt's then-president, Mohamed Morsi, warned that if his country's Nile water "diminishes by one drop then our blood is the alternative", though he insisted he was not "calling for war [– yet]". Fortunately, Ethiopia's new Prime Minister, Abiy Ahmed, further minimised the possibility of conflict. Compared with his predecessor, Ahmed has proven more successful in facilitating successful negotiations with Egypt and Sudan,[31] which was evidenced in the 2018 agreement to continue dialogue in bi-annual meetings.

During a news conference in Cairo last year, Ahmed promised Egyptians, "I swear to God, we will never hurt you", after Egyptian President Abdel Fattah Sisi pressed him to swear in front of the Egyptian people that he would not harm the country's Nile water share. Sisi, for his part, conceded there was no "military solution" and called ongoing talks a breakthrough; "We managed to actually find a number of win-win approaches", he said.

In any event, no matter how *wrong* a stakeholder situation might have gone, the Four-Step Approach may still be used to remedy the predicament; and here is a concrete example!

The author was appointed to project manage the launching of the first All-Africa Local Government Congress, which was scheduled to take place in Tshwane (South Africa) in May 2005; in fact, the event was initially scheduled for 2004, but failed to materialise. As of March 2005, there was still no sign that the event (project) would in anyway be on-track.

As soon as the new project team (led by the author) took charge of the event, a sad situation arose with the previous team (staffed by the City Council of Tshwane itself) taking exception to being unfairly removed from their treasured project; they mobilised to literally disown the newly appointed team – the stage was lit for *smouldering* conflicts.

Aware of this undercurrent of tension, the new team not only undertook to clarify the project scope and its requirements, but also swiftly proceeded to identify who the main stakeholders were *at that stage of the project*, both internally at the City of Tshwane and across the continent. This included would-be delegates and government agencies, many of which were not identified and/or ever engaged by the previous project team.

Purposely, those disgruntled folks and their "sponsors and supporters" were included.

However, when interviewing the many identified stakeholders, it transpired that some of the disgruntled former team members indeed had legitimate concerns (e.g., bonus payment), and some others could still add value to the project. Many individuals were just *taking sides*, due to their relationship (or lack thereof) with influential figures in the council.

The author, thus, advised that these individuals should be incorporated in the *re-structured* project team, but only based on their capacity/ability to perform project activities. Moreover, he established clearer roles and responsibilities, including engagement protocols among team members and with external parties. The team also invited state officials that usually attended to logistics issues on high-profile events to *actively* support the project.

Weekly steering committee meetings (where Tshwane senior officials were included) were separated from the "operational" review meetings intended to assess progress; thus, risks were identified and allocated to the "best possible person" to manage them. For instance, instead of begging local XYZ car dealers for a fleet sponsorship, the team spoke directly to the XYZ national head office and a VIP fleet was arranged within days.

By fittingly reverting to the proposed Four-Step Approach, this prestigious event, which was chaired by the then Nigerian president (H.E. Obasanjo), turned out to be a *resounding* success!

11 Conclusions

The Large Infrastructure Projects (LIPs) industry has recently experienced a "rude awakening" to the reality that a failure of Stakeholder Management (SM) will more often than not lead to a failure of the project. It has become clearer from the foregoing discussions that a lack of (or any conceivably inadequate) Stakeholder Engagement is an open invitation for disaster. For a disgruntled stakeholder will eventually "throw a spanner in the works"; many large projects have come to a grinding halt as a result of flawed or lack of Stakeholder Engagement. This happens when the "stakes" are perceived as a matter of survival and, therefore, are presumed to be exceptionally high.

As was stated in previous chapters, "stake" is the operative word in stakeholder; "and when the stakes are high (as often in LIPs), conflicts are likely to arise ... and to persist". The project team must be equipped to understand their nature and to apply remedies. It follows that Stakeholder Management should seek to achieve "well-orchestrated engagements" with key project stakeholders to secure their participation and support.

The construction industry has developed a great difficulty in coping with the increasing complexity of major construction projects. Then again, still owing to the complexities involved, traditional approaches to managing stakeholders have similarly developed serious difficulties in dealing with large and complex projects. One such difficulty involves "solving a set of interlocking issues and constraints by multiple stakeholders".

It is therefore noted that Stakeholder Management is by no means a straightforward, systematic process; it combines "methodical" and "expressive" aspects. The expressive part should involve maintaining "thrust" (i.e., a commitment to project objectives), and engendering "trust" (i.e., from each bona-fide stakeholder), and gathering "learnings" (i.e., on changing patterns of behaviour in the network of stakeholders). For this reason:

The combination of [1]technical ... and [2]social sciences ... has created a dual approach in which the well-developed project oriented approach focusing on project leadership, planning and financial engineering is combined with a social sciences approach that is focusing much more on the complex process of implementation and the variety of stakeholders.

Effective project delivery is a team effort across the Systems-of-Interest. A "structured" Four-Step Stakeholder Management Approach is recommended that relies on Systems Thinking and "leadership" to unravel the complexities so prevalent in Large Infrastructure Projects. This approach comprises four *overlapping* steps as follows:

(1) Stakeholder Identification;
(2) Stakeholder Analysis;
(3) Stakeholder Strategy and Plan; and
(4) Stakeholder Engagement.

This SM process will equip the project manager and team members with the necessary wherewithal for devising a suitable response to stakeholder "attitudes", including a deliberate choice to refrain from communicating and/or acting, or even from retaliating. The point of SM is to win over any adverse stakeholders and turn them into supporters.

Whereas "Stakeholder Engagement" is the ultimate step in the proposed approach, that step alone might not yield the required results of "securing input" and "securing buy-in" (i.e., dual purposes) on the part of conflicting stakeholders. It takes concerted efforts and preparative work in the prior steps of "Stakeholder Identification", "Stakeholder Analysis", and "Stakeholder Strategy and Plan" to lay the fertile ground for successful engagements. Nobody should identify, analyse, or plan stakeholders just for the sake of it, as a formality!

Any form of inadequacies or shortcomings in those preparative steps of the Stakeholder Management process transpires downstream, during the ultimate "Stakeholder Engagement". For that reason, several SM tools and techniques have been discussed, mostly as far as "Stakeholder Identification" and "Stakeholder Analysis" are concerned. This minimises incidences of stakeholders being overlooked or wrongly analysed, leading to defective engagements – which would imperil the required input and buy-in.

Thus, Stakeholder Management *basically* consists of devising a strategy and a plan for engaging stakeholders in order to secure relevant input, as well as dependable buy-in on their part – based on a particular "Concept of Operations" (ConOps) and in line with their expectations, concerns, needs, and desires, as well as their power, interests, degree of influence, and legitimacy. It follows that the effective identification of stakeholders and their requirements (i.e., Stakeholder Requirements) shall flow from the selected ConOps.

Instances of failed Stakeholder Management are discussed in this book to explain that focusing only on technical aspects of a large project is somewhat counterintuitive, and to illustrate how failing to manage project stakeholders will more often than not cause the project to fail. In a number of such examples, it is highlighted that *persistently* addressing the "hard/technical" issues on the project cannot yield good results, because the "soft issues" pertaining to Stakeholder Management are left unattended.

An exploration of ten infamous "abandoned shopping malls" has shown projects that could otherwise have been successful ending up as failures due to the actions or attitudes of "in-operations" stakeholders that were ignored or not anticipated at the planning stages.

In most instances, attempts were made to resuscitate the shopping mall through some "physical" interventions, but to no avail – a proper SM process was definitively required!

Stakeholder Management should consider the "operability" (i.e., ConOps) of the "system". Therefore, project stakeholders should be engaged across the Context System (i.e., Systems-of-Interest), and throughout the "system" lifecycle, and maintained "current" through a constant scanning of the environment. Further, Large Infrastructure Projects being sociotechnical endeavours, both technical and human aspects should be addressed.

The Port Elizabeth Bus Rapid Transit (BRT) system has been adopted as an improvement on regular bus services through the combination of features like infrastructure change to achieve better operation speeds and service reliability. Before taking a decision on implementing the awaited BRT system, the transport needs of the residents in various communities around Nelson Mandela Bay Municipality area were observed through a public consultation process (based mostly on "technical factors") in the years 2010 and 2011. As result, the infrastructure (which would also fail the "operational readiness" test) proved *unappealing* to users (i.e., main project stakeholders); the BRT is said to be less effective, even to build more buy-in from customers, especially private car users.[2]

The example of the Ethiopian Dam project is quite remarkable. It proves beyond any doubt that as a result of project scope/activities, stakeholders surface in adjacent "systems", but not necessarily in proximity of space or time. While the completion of the Grand Ethiopian

Renaissance Dam is set to provide electricity to the 60% of Ethiopia's population that currently has no access, it will *similarly* disrupt freshwater supply downstream in the fertile strip along the Nile for farming and water – although the doomsday event will only take place in 3–15 years. At the moment, 95% of Egypt's population reside in the Nile Valley.

This is a beautiful instance of Systems Dynamics (i.e., complexities) playing themselves out in the planning and delivery of infrastructure projects. If anything, the example lends credence to the notion of applying Systems Thinking and Systems Engineering concepts, principles, or practices in managing stakeholders in large and complex projects (e.g., LIPs) – as the proposed Four-Step Stakeholder Management Approach would recommend.

In the fictitious project alluded to in Chapter 5 (i.e., to develop a 7000 km rail/road belt from Lagos to Mombasa), using the Systems Thinking approach has helped to identify a number of "unsuspected" stakeholders, who might otherwise have been overlooked or ignored in the project. Surely, overlooking and failing to "engage" powerful stakeholders such as the drug syndicates, environmental protection agencies, global oil traders, tribal authorities, religious leaders, and armed militias is an invitation to trouble.

While identifying stakeholders accurately is crucial to project success, analysing them *insightfully* is equally important in order to understand their "stakes" and their mutual or intersecting "relationships" across the Systems-of-Interest. Without these elements, the dynamics of emerging behaviours will be misinterpreted, if not missed altogether. Hence, in addition to "Stakeholder Analysis" tools and techniques found in the literature, two E6PC "in-house" tools are introduced to assist in exploring *relationships*. They are as follows:

(i)   The Occasional Friends and Foes (OFF) Diagram:

   It depicts "relationships of affinity" among agents as identified in the ecology, with a focus on those that cross the divide between the "friends" and "foes" of the project.

(ii)   The Lines of Influence Network (LOIN) Diagram:

   It depicts "relationships of influence" (assuming a one-way channel of influence) to determine potential epicentres of influence, i.e., "who" could influence other agents the most, and vice-versa, "who" is most vulnerable to influence in the project ecology.

Moreover, since Stakeholder Management plays an integral role in project delivery, it is crucial that its activities/deliverables are incorporated and dovetailed in other project management processes. For "Stakeholder Management activities should be managed at the same level of definition and with the same diligence as the above-mentioned PM processes". Hence, a mapping of SM activities across the project lifecycle is discussed, deliberately breaking down scope and deliverables of the SM process for each project phase. For instance, "Identification" should be addressed at the Conceptual phase (FEL-1) of the project, while "Strategy and Plan" ought to be confirmed at the Feasibility phase (FEL-3).

The foregoing considerations, discussions, and (actual) examples have surely settled the notion that "managing projects means managing stakeholders", while also introducing an ethical perspective, i.e., stakeholders have legitimate rights regardless of their power to influence the project. This makes Stakeholder Management more inclusive and/or receptive. Many authors have broadened the idea of stakeholder beyond the traditional concept of "power to influence" to also include the powerless, the voiceless, and other "vulnerable" entities in their inclusive definition of stakeholders. This stance shifts the paradigm from "Management *of* Stakeholders" to "Management *for* Stakeholders".

12 Practical applications

Readers who do not wish to "practice" Stakeholder Management (SM) may skip this section.

Hardly any endeavour can be implemented without having to deal with stakeholders that must be "managed" somehow or other – whether it is establishing a new church, starting a business, hosting a major event, or building infrastructure such as a power plant, reservoir, road/rail network, hospital, shopping mall, school, or stadium.

The project manager and team members will be expected to not only understand the necessity of SM, but more importantly to acquire the right skills for *fruitfully* conducting SM. Above all, Large Infrastructure Projects (LIPs) entail diverse stakeholders that must be engaged for relevant input and dependable buy-in.

Therefore, LIPs practitioners require as many opportunities as their circumstances might dictate to master the crucial skill of managing project stakeholders; part of which is systematic (i.e., scientific), and part of which is expressive (i.e., artistic). This mastery does not happen automatically but rather requires commitment and a lot of effort.

Accordingly, a number of practical exercises are included in this chapter to afford an opportunity for project managers and other team members to "grow into this thing". They seek to expose project teams to various facets of Stakeholder Management; and by simply applying one's mind repeatedly on the issues raised, the project team member will gain sufficient understanding of the intricacies of stakeholder dynamics in order to play a *meaningful* role in the SM process throughout the entire project lifecycle.

While the practical exercises provided here seek to cover most, if not all the aspects of Stakeholder Management, they might already begin to reveal that different people could have different inclinations, innate abilities, or levels of appetite for a specific portion of the recommended Four-Step Stakeholder Management Approach. Some team members will enjoy getting involved in the "Identification" and/or "Analysis" steps of the process, whereas others might rather excel in the "Strategy and Plan" bit, and still others will find delight in the "Engagement" part. Therefore, in making it a team effort, the project manager will succeed in mustering diverse *strengths* across the team.

Once the project team seizes the opportunity of the first project (preferably under the guidance of someone familiar with the process) and gets their hands dirty, the rest (e.g., gaining confidence) will follow in due course, even as they rise from "rookie" to master!

12.1 Practical exercise no 1

The PMBoK[47] (Fifth Edition) clearly states the following:

> Stakeholders are persons or organisations (e.g., customers, sponsors, the performing organisation, or the public), who are actively involved in the project or whose interest may be positively or negatively affected by the performance or the completion of the project. Stakeholders may also exert influence over the project, its deliverables, and the project team.

Without attempting in any way to overly simplify the above definition, it is also worth mentioning R.E. Freeman's concise rendition, "A stakeholder in an organisation [project] is (by definition) any group or individual who can affect or is affected by the achievement of the organisation's [project's] objectives".[21] It is therefore worth noting, as Mitchell[41] ("Toward a theory of stakeholder identification and salience: Defining the principle of who and what really counts") has also suggested, that the decision about how to define stakeholders is consequential, as it affects who and what counts.

Question no 1.1

It is suggested that one of the main activities to be performed by the project team at the FEL-1 Phase consists of developing "System Requirements". Thus, using the *Four-Step Stakeholder Management Approach* and the *Project Stakeholder Identification Matrix* (extracts of which are illustrated in Figure 12.1 and Table 12.1), you are expected to identify all the relevant stakeholders for the "Inter-SADC Railway Link" project connecting Gaborone (Botswana) to Maputo (Mozambique). Please indicate those project stakeholders that shall provide input into the requirements formulation process at Concept phase, FEL-1.

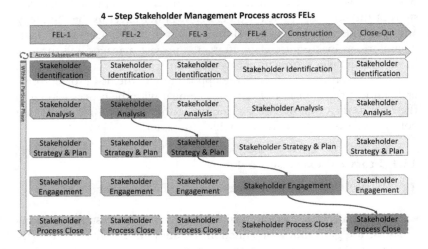

Figure 12.1 The Four-Step Stakeholder Management Process across FELs

For the below SIM (see Table 12.1) consider including the following: *Processes of delivery (e.g., funding, planning, design, construction, utilisation, maintenance, disposal); Functions (e.g., rail transportation for cargos, commuters, and emergency logistics during war/disaster); and Outcomes (e.g., traffic across countries, affecting border-control, trade and customs, Health and Safety).*

- What difference does it make (benefit of) having *procedurally* identified all project stakeholders at FEL-1? Could it have been the same if such project stakeholders were rather identified at a FEL-3 (Feasibility) stage? Or even just at Construction?
- While the proposed **Four-Step Process** suggests performing a "Stakeholder Analysis" at FEL-2, would you still encourage the project team to proceed with subsequent steps – and closeout – as per Figure 12.1 – during the current FEL-1 with regards to those project activities (such as "system" requirements formulation, options identification, identification of major risks) that take place at this particular stage?

Question no 1.2

- Having answered Question No 1.1, how would you reconcile the "Analysis" process to the "optioneering" (i.e., discussing solution-options to select the most-viable option) that is expected to take place during the FEL-2 (Pre-Feasibility) phase?

Table 12.1 The Project Stakeholder Identification Matrix (SIM)

Stake(s)/claim(s)/interest(s) on the project

Function(s), Process(es), or outcome(s)	*Users/ consumers*	*Beneficiaries*	*Suppliers*	*Influencers*	*Sponsors*	*Affected parties*	*Right holders*	*Legislators*	*Decision-makers*	*Project workforce*
Φ1										
...										
Φ5										
...										
Φ9										

• What "additional" benefits would you argue arise from using the SIM template as compared with other "Identification" tools? What other purpose could the template serve in the ensuing phases? Shall "Analysis" ever serve to vindicate "Identification"? (Table 12.2).

Question no 1.3

Consider the anticipated 7210 kilometres Cape-to-Cairo standard-gauge railway line to be spearheaded by the Infrastructure Planning Unit of the New Partnership for Africa's Development (NEPAD). The project still being at the Conceptual (FEL-1) phase, three different "Concept of Operations" (ConOps) for the *distributed* locomotive traction are being explored as follows:

(i)   Diesel Locomotives, with sufficient "accompanying" fuel-tanker wagons;
(ii) Diesel Locomotives, to be refuelled at various Diesel depots along the route;
(iii) Electric Locomotives, with power supplied by various providers along the route.

   • Discuss how the contemplated ConOps might involve different stakeholders.
   • Discuss to what extent the stakeholder situation might affect risk management.
   • What roles and responsibilities could the NEPAD play in managing stakeholders?

12.2 Practical exercise no 2

Stakeholder Identification is the first and, thus, the most critical phase of the process.

Some organisational activities are large and complex, and may affect many stakeholders. For example, construction of public facilities or national infrastructure projects will affect private citizens, landowners, and the natural and historical environment. For such projects, it is essential to recognise and accept that there will be large numbers of stakeholders identified. There is often an unconscious boundary on what a "good number" of stakeholders can be – this is stakeholder myopia. It is important for the team and for their management to understand that while the initial number of stakeholders identified may appear unwieldy or overwhelming, step 2: prioritise provides

Table 12.2 Template Project Stakeholder Identification Matrix

Processes, functions, or outcomes across SoIs	Stake(s)/claim(s)/interest(s) on the project [part II]								
	Users/ consumers	*Beneficiaries*	*Suppliers*	*Influencers*	*Sponsors*	*Affected parties*	*Right holders*	*Legislators*	*Decision-makers*	*Project workforce*
Process 1									
Process 2									
Function 1									
Function 2									
Outcome 1									
Outcome 2									

a structured and logical means to prioritise the key stakeholders for the current time.

Dr Lynda Bourne[12], DPM, PMP

Question no 2.1

- Discuss this quote in terms of defining the "Systems-of-Interest" and Stakeholder Identification. What implication would stakeholder myopia have on the project?
- As the project manager, what organisational arrangement would you rely on to assure that the right (i.e., relevant) stakeholders are identified as early as FEl-1? What discussions, therefore, would you have with the appointed risk manager?

Question no 2.2

Dankie Boluka has just relocated to the town of Afrikanaville, in the Ngulube District Municipality; the newly appointed city manager has requested a meeting with Dankie to enlist his assistance in addressing the *thorny*, notorious issue of the "Billing Scheme":

> The city has lost face ... and faith in our billing system; our constituency is always angry with erratic billing, which then gives residents a good excuse to refuse paying ... revenue collection is falling apart – We have decided to do away with utility billing. We are looking for a "system" that will allow the city to link supply and payment of water and electricity to rates and taxes: debit-orders effected for rates and taxes will then include payments for water and electricity, and provide residents a certain amount of consumption. The system shall inform residents via SMS of their consumption status.

- Based on this conversation, the city manager expects Dankie Boluka to advise him of plausible stakeholders so he can allocate teams to start gauging their support and negotiating with them even before he announces the "Billing Scheme" to the public at the next Budget Speech (the team will use the Stakeholder Identification Matrix template of Question No 1.1).
- Dankie is a Stakeholder Management practitioner, therefore, what specific stakeholders should he advise the city manager to refrain from engaging before any public announcement is made to that effect?
- What internal departments (within the municipality) should the city manager "restructure" to accommodate this scheme?

Question no 2.3

Consider the essential elements of SM at some point in the lifecycle of this project:

(i) Forward planning the engagement as one would do in any complex activity, with a schedule and sufficient staff with the right capabilities;

(ii) Weekly and monthly reports prepared by the lead Engagement Officer detailing the number and status of complaints and any outstanding issues sent to the Community Representative;

(iii) Demonstrating that people's opinions and ideas are receiving serious attention, whether by "designing-out" identified risks, "designing-in" additional economic or social benefits, or incorporating the views of stakeholders in testing the feasibility of various design and risk management options.

• Discuss at which step(s) of the recommended Four-Step Approach or project phase(s) these stakeholder-related activities should apply – and what benefits they bring.

• What specific advice would you provide to Dankie to prevent him from falling into some kind of "stakeholder myopia" trap? Understanding that failed Stakeholder Management will probably entail the failure of the project itself, how will you advise Dankie to reconcile Risk Management and Stakeholder Identification?

• Dankie is a risk manager by profession, therefore, would you find it appropriate that he should also drive Stakeholder Management or will you recommend he focuses on Risk Management in support of somebody else being appointed to focus on SM?

12.3 Practical exercise no 3

"Engagement" is the decisive step of the SM process – the place to put the plan to effect!

Stakeholder Engagement

Stakeholder Engagement, by which I mean talking with and listening to stakeholders in a style that works for them, and not something as narrow as just communicating with people or as invasive as managing them – Engage with your stakeholders; don't try to control them.

Alan Ferguson[20]

Influence/Interest Matrix (Figure 12.2)

- *Interest.* The vertical axis is the interest of the stakeholder in the project or programme. You can think of this as the impact the project/programme has on the stakeholder: if a project/programme has more impact, the stakeholder is probably going to be more interested in the project/programme.
- *Influence.* The horizontal axis reflects how much influence stakeholders have (or is perceived to have) over the project/programme. However, a stakeholder group may have a great deal of power but choose not to use that power in relation to the project/programme.
- *Banding.* This Interest–Influence Grid (referring to Figure 7.2) gives some simple examples of different types of interactions with different stakeholders. The figure also recommends some generic and indicative strategies on how to manage such interactions.

Question no 3.1

- Based on Stakeholder Identification conducted under Question No 1.1 [Practical exercise No 1], conduct a SWOT Analysis and plot out key stakeholders on the Influence/Interest Matrix provided on the next page. Use the information gathered to develop the Stakeholder Management Strategy and its related Plan.

  1. How will you align the EIA to "Stakeholder Analysis" and to "Optioneering" at FEL-2?
  2. What insight will you draw from the SWOT in terms of stakeholder "attitudes"?

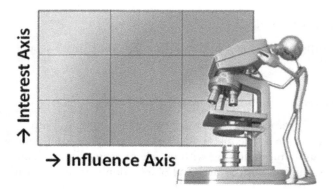

Figure 12.2 The Influence–Interest Grid

3. How will you summarise your engagement strategy to the project board? Give examples of "messages" to various stakeholders, with benefits or disbenefits.

4. Is there a difference (i.e., by definition, in practice) between the two notions of "Communication Strategy" and "Engagement Strategy" in the context of SM?

5. Which of the following "headings" should not feature in your SM Plan, Why?

   (i) Schedule of engagements
   (ii) Records of stakeholder feedback
   (iii) Communication policies
   (iv) Objectives of each engagement
   (v) Key message(s) and approach to delivery thereof
   (vi) Audience for each engagement

Question no 3.2

- What can turn your stakeholder's "Strategy and Plan" *wrong* at FEL-2? At FEL-3? How will you remedy such situations? What specific PMBoK Knowledge Areas will you refer to and how would you incorporate and apply them in project delivery?

- In addition to the *generic* strategies provided in the Matrix, what else should inform your "strategy"? What (adverse) implications could a flawed Engagement Strategy cause to the project outcome? Should that happen, how will you remedy it?

- Why is it crucial to explore and discuss any *relationships* between and among project activities and/or stakeholders, as well as between them and the project environment to contribute to the crafting of an effective engagement "strategy"? In which way does an adequate "Plan" contribute to a successful engagement?

A particular version of the "Influence versus Interest" Matrix (with a set of generic engagement strategies) is provided below, as adapted from Alan Ferguson[20] (see Figure 12.3).

12.4 Practical exercise no 4

Refer to the actual account of the Dakota pipeline project from an Al Jazeera documentary:[3]

In September 2014, the "Standing Rock Sioux" tribe – a Native American tribe – found out that an American oil company had planned on

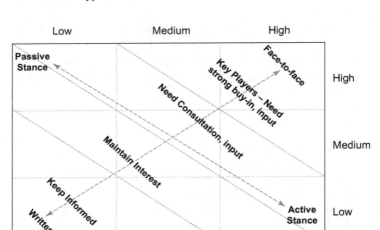

Figure 12.3 Generic engagement strategies as per the Influence–Interest Grid

building an oil pipeline under a river and over a land portion that they had believed to be sacred [near the Mississippi River].

The oil company was told that this action went against treaty boundaries [i.e., Dakota means treaty] and that this "was something that the tribe was not supporting". The pipeline would disrupt an ancestral site and "villagers" who lived there believed that the project would disrupt their activities – and the planned pipeline was going against who they were as a people. The pipeline was said to be a techno-logical marvel and an engineering feat, but it was revealed that the US army corps regarded the complaints and grievances that the tribe brought forth during consultations as "a formality to be overcome rather than any real dialogue". Hence, after being shown the "sacred sites" the agency would still fail to document or register such ances-tral places for protection.

The Standing Rock Sioux tribe were not the only stakeholders that did not agree with this project. Three federal agencies [i.e., the E.P.A., the Department of Interior, and the Advisory Council on Historic Preservation] expressed concerns, as they felt that "the army corps never properly consulted with the tribe or considered the risks to the water and land". In April 2015, when it became clear that the army corps was not listening to them [i.e., failure to properly engage the stakeholders], the tribe decided to erect a protest-camp near the planned building-site of the pipeline. As of July, after almost 8 months of failing to engage the tribe as "significant" stakeholders, this camp grew in momentum. Even so, things were still going in whatever direction the oil company had wanted; this caused the tribe to take the army corps to federal court – but to no avail!

However, after a short video "asking for help and support of other tribes – and anyone willing to assist" was filmed and released, more "peaceful protests" began as a form of non-compliance to the pipeline project and this movement grew rapidly. Members of other Native tribes in similar predicaments or had faced this manner of "bullying" by big corporations stood in solidarity with the Standing Rock Sioux tribe and it was discovered (or once again brought to light) that this "injustice" had been happening to Native American tribes for decades and probably centuries. In September that year, protestors [i.e., stakeholders] were violently harassed [i.e., instead of re-identification, analysis and a new engagement plan]; maybe the oil and pipeline corporation thought that "vigorously fighting the stakeholders" might lead them into accepting the project.

It was only then that the federal government intervened by deciding "to consult more with the Sioux tribe before permits were issued". But peaceful protests in the camps continued and the "private security" operatives carried on harassing the protestors [i.e., stakeholders]. On September 2, details of the "sacred sites" were submitted to the federal court, as well as other relevant information; but the next day, more "sacred sites" were destroyed and, again, protestors were harassed, unfairly beaten, and had dogs unleashed on them. The Sioux tribe's elders and allies were outraged.

This led to an investigation being held by the State Historical Society, which *wrongly* concluded that no human remains or burial sites were impacted. But this inquiry was, again, made without consulting the Standing Rock tribe. However, after a follow-up visit that included the stakeholders, it was then discovered that indeed "sacred sites" had been tampered with, desecrated or destroyed altogether. Still, the state disagreed with these new findings; and for that reason, allowed construction works to continue.

In December, after months of stakeholder neglect and/or abuse, the US government agreed to a Full Environmental Review and promised that no further sites would be desecrated, tampered with, or destroyed, and conceded to the re-routing the pipeline. But on the day after the announcement, the victory of the stakeholders was short-lived as the government and the oil pipeline company refused to be interviewed; but their statements made it clear that drilling was to continue and none of the "original" plans were to be altered – thus, stakeholders continued to protest against the project.

Despite the project being designed to be an engineering feat, the Sioux tribe were not identified as relevant stakeholders. So even after problems arose, these stakeholders were still discarded, forgetting that while they only had moderate power, the Sioux tribe had a high influence in the continuity of this project. Failure to correctly identify or engage stakeholders caused many "setbacks" for the pipeline project, as time was lost during court appearances. Money was also wastefully spent on private security. Hence, the reputation, as well as integrity of the project, was severely compromised.

Question no 4.1

- What Stakeholder Management errors might have brought about this predicament? How would you convince the US federal agencies concerned that their Stakeholder Management process has failed, which could result in the project failing altogether?
- Consider yourself being the appointed Stakeholder Manager on this project at this juncture; how would you proceed to successfully apply the "Four-Step Approach to SM"? Would you consider using an OFF or any such systemigrams to analyse stakeholders?

Personal reflections

References

1. Ackermann, Fran and Eden, Colin, 2011. Strategic management of stakeholders: theory and practice. *Long Range Planning*, 44(3), pp.179–196.
2. Adewumi, E. and Allopi, D., 2014. Critical assessment of Port Elizabeth bus rapid transit system. *Journal of Architecture and Engineering*, 2, pp.2321–8193.
3. Al Jazeera, 2016. *Standing rock and the battle beyond.* [video] Available at: https://www.youtube.com/watch?v=RX-3jdXa46U [Accessed 18 October 2019].
4. Ambler, S., 2004. *The object primer.* Cambridge, UK: Cambridge University Press.
5. Archibald, R., Di Filippo, I. and Di Filippo, D., December 2012. The six phase comprehensive project life cycle model includes the project incubation-feasibility phase and the post-project evaluation phase. *PM World Journal.* [online].
6. Baccarini, D., 1996. The concept of project complexity – a review. *International Journal of Project Management*, 14(4), pp.201–204.
7. Baker, E., 2006. It's all about ME (managing expectations)! *Paper presented at PMI® Global Congress 2006—North America, Seattle, WA.* Newtown Square, PA: Project Management Institute.
8. Becker, F., 2002. Organisational dilemmas and workplace solutions. *Journal of Corporate Real Estate*, 4(2), pp.129–149.
9. Bell, S., Neville, B. and Menguc, B., 2003. Stakeholder salience reloaded: operationalising corporate social responsibility. In: *ANZMAC Conference Proceedings*, Adelaide, pp.1883–1889.
10. Bertelsen, S., 2004. Construction management in a complexity perspective. In: *1st International SCRI Symposium*, March 30th–31st, University of Salford, UK, pp.1–7.
11. Bourne, L., 2009. *Why stakeholders matter – Chief Executive Officer.* [online] Available at: http://www.the-chiefexecutive.com/features/feature68469/index.html [Accessed 14 October 2019].
12. Bourne, L., 2010. Why is stakeholder management so difficult? In: *EAN University Virtual Conference.* Bogota, Columbia, p.123. [online] Available at: https://mosaicprojects.com.au/Resources_Papers_123.html [Accessed 29 April 2018].

13. Bourne, L. *Stakeholder relationship management maturity.* 1st ed. [ebook] Melbourne: Mosaic Projects. [online] Available at: https://mosaicprojects.co m.au/PDF_Papers/P175_Implementing_effective_stakeholder_engagemen t.pdf [Accessed 14 October 2019].

14. Cleland, D. and Ireland, L., 2002. *Project management: strategic design and implementation.* 4th ed. Tennessee: McGraw-Hill, pp.4–7, 67–69.

15. Cooke-Davies, T., 2011. Aspects of complexity: managing projects in a complex world. Paper presented at PMI® Global Congress 2011—North America, Dallas, TX. Newtown Square, PA: Project Management Institute

16. Crouhy, M., Mark, R. and Galai, D., 2009. *The essentials of risk management.* New York, NY: McGraw-Hill.

17. De Meuse, K., 2009. *A comparative analysis of the Korn/Ferry T7 model with other popular team models.* [ebook] Los Angeles, CA: The Korn/Ferry Institute. [online] Available at: https://www.kornferry.com/media/lominger_pdf/teams whitepaper080409.pdf [Accessed 14 October 2019].

18. Director: Mineral Development, 1999. Gauteng region v save the vaal environment and others 1999 (2) SA 709 (SCA).

19. Eduardo, C., Dergint, D. and Hatakeyama, K., 2000. Project-based organizations as complex adaptive systems. 2004, pp.1–12.

20. Ferguson, A., 2014. *MSP for dummies.* Chichester, London: John Wiley & Sons.

21. Freeman, R., 1984. *Strategic management.* 1st ed. New York, NY: Pitman Publishing.

22. Glass, R.J., Ames, A.L., Stubblefield, W.A., Conrad, S.H., Maffitt, S.L., et al., 2008. *Sandia National Laboratories: a roadmap for the complex adaptive systems of systems (CASoS) engineering initiative.* Albuquerque, NM: Sandia National Laboratories, SAND 2008-4651.

23. Goodman, M., 1997. *Designing a systems thinking intervention.* Waltham, MA: Pegasus Communications.

24. Gould, S., 1998. *The mismeasure of man.* New York, NY: W.W. Norton.

25. Haskins, C. and Forsberg, K., 2011. *Systems engineering handbook.* Seattle, WA: INCOSE.

26. Hellriegel, D., Slocum, J. and Cheng, C., 1996. *Management.* Cincinnati, OH: South-Western College Publishing.

27. Hood, C., 2008. *Requirements management.* Berlin: Springer.

28. Hovland, I. 2005. *Successful communication: a toolkit for researchers and civil society organisations.* [online] Available at: www.odi.org.uk/publications/toolkits/rap id/tools2.pdf [Accessed 17 January 2020].

29. IIBA, 2009. *A guide to the business analysis body of knowledger.* Toronto: International Institute of Business Analysis / Kevin Brennan Edition 2. ISBN 0981129218, 9780981129211.

30. INCOSE, 2012. *Guide for the application of systems engineering in large infrastructure projects.* 1st ed. San Diego, CA: INCOSE. [online] Available at: https://ww w.incose.org/docs/default-source/Working-Groups/infrastructure-wg-docu ments/guide_for_the_application_of_se_in_large-infrastructure-projects-2012 -0625-to-approved-update-2013-0417.pdf?sfvrsn=bc2c82c6_10 [Accessed 29 April 2018].

31. Islam, S., 2019. The Ethiopians are building a massive dam, and Egypt is worried. *Los Angeles Times.* [online] Available at: https://www.latimes.com/world/la-fg-egypt-ethiopia-nile-dam-20190408-story.html [Accessed 18 October 2019].

32. ISO/IEC 15288:2008, 2008. *Systems and software engineering — system life cycle processes.* 2nd ed. Geneva.

33. Krygiel, A.J., 1999. *Behind the wizard's curtain: an integration environment for a system of systems.* Washington, DC: National Defence University.

34. Mabelo, P.B., 2016. *Application of systems engineering concepts as enhancements to the project lifecycle methodology.* Masters. University of Witwatersrand.

35. Mabelo, P.B. and Sunjka, B., 2017. Application of systems engineering concepts to enhance project lifecycle methodologies. *South African Journal of Industrial Engineering,* 28(3), pp. 30–45.

36. Maqsood, T., Finegan, A. and Walker, D.H.T., 2009. A conceptual model for exploring knowledge channelisation from sources of innovation in construction organizations: extending the role of knowledge management. *Proceedings of the 19th Annual ARCOM Conference, University of Brighton, 3–5 September 2003.* Reading: ARCOM, ISBN 0953416186 *Management.*

37. Martin, J., 2004. 3.1.2 the seven samurai of systems engineering: dealing with the complexity of 7 interrelated systems. *INCOSE International Symposium,* 14(1), pp.459–470.

38. Meadows, D., Randers, J. and Meadows, D., 1972. *The limits to growth.* White River Junction, VT: Potomac Associates, pp.91–92.

39. Measurement Working Group International Council on Systems Engineering (INCOSE), 2010. *Systems Engineering Measurement Primer. A basic introduction to measurement concepts and use for systems engineering.* 2nd ed. San Diego, CA: Measurement Working Group International Council on Systems Engineering (INCOSE).

40. Merrow, E., 2011. *Industrial megaprojects.* 1st ed. New Jersey: Wiley.

41. Mitchell, Ronald K., Agle, Bradley R., and Wood, Donna J. 1997. Toward a theory of stakeholder identification and salience: defining the principle of who and what really counts. *Academy of Management Review* 22, pp.853–886.

42. Morris, C., 2013. *Project management mentoring: learning to accept accountability when projects go wrong.* [video] Available at: https://www.youtube.com/watch?v=YioMxuu3L_g [Accessed 21 October 2019].

43. NETLIPSE, 2008. *Managing large infrastructure projects (research on best practices and lessons learnt in large infrastructure projects in Europe).* NETLIPSE Report. [online] Available at: http://netlipse.eu/netlipse [Accessed 15 September 2014].

44. Office of the Deputy Under Secretary of Defence for Acquisition and Technology, Systems and Software Engineering, 2008. *Systems engineering guide for systems of systems, version 1.0.* Washington, DC: ODUSD(A&T) SSE.

45. Paul, D., Cadle, J. and Yeates, D., 2017. *Business analysis.* Swindon: British Informatics Society Limited.

46. Project Management Institute, 2015. *Business analysis for practitioners: a practice guide.* Pennsylvania: Project Management Institute. ISBN: 978-1-62825-069-5.

47. Project Management Institute, 2013. *A guide to the project management body of knowledge (PMBoK guide).* 5th ed. Pennsylvania: Project Management Institute.

48. Renard, Y., 2004. *Guidelines for stakeholder identification and analysis.* Laventille, Trinidad: Caribbean Natural Resources Institute.

49. Rotach, D., 2019. *Systems and conflict.* [video] Available at: https://www.you tube.com/watch?v=fY3Wns18BDo [Accessed 18 October 2019].

50. Ryen, E., 2008. *Overview of the systems engineering process.* Intelligent Transportation Systems, North Dakota, Department of Transportation. [online] Available at: https://www.dot.nd.gov/divisions/maintenance/docs/ OverviewOfSEA.pdf [Accessed 25 June 2016].

51. Scott, Z., 2012. *9 laws of effective systems engineering.* White Paper. Virginia: Vitech Corporation. [online] www.vitechcorp.com. Available at: http://www .vitechcorp.com/resources/white_papers [Accessed 25 June 2016].

52. SEBoK, n.d. *Stakeholder needs and requirements.* [online] Available at: http:// sebokwiki.org/wiki [Accessed 21 April 2015].

53. Senge, P.M., 2006. *The fifth discipline: the art and practice of the learning organization.* New York, NY: Crown Publishing Group.

54. Shukla, V.S. and QBI Institute Business Analysis Training, 2015. *Stakeholder analysis and management.* [video] Available at: https://www.youtube.com/w atch?v=dE4Ufze7JBo [Accessed 21 October 2019].

55. Slack, N., Brandon-Jones, A. and Johnston, R., 2010. *Operations management.* 6th ed. Harlow, UK: Prentice Hall-Financial Times.

56. Smith, B., 2005. *Developing an using concept of operations in transportation management systems.* [ebook] Charlottesville, VA: U.S. Department of Transportation. [online] Available at: https://tmcpfs.ops.fhwa.dot.gov/cfprojects/uploaded_fil es/conops_tms_handbook.pdf [Accessed 18 October 2019].

57. Standish Group, 1995. The Chaos Report (1994). The Chaos Report. [online] Available at: http://www.standishgroup.com/sample_research_files/chaos_rep ort_1994.pdf [Accessed 25 June 2016].

58. Steyn, H., 2016. *Project management – a multi-disciplinary approach.* 4th ed. Pretoria: FPM Publishing.

59. Sussman, J., 2007. *Course materials for ESD.04J frameworks and models in engineering systems.* Springfield, MA: MIT.

60. Sussman, J. and Mosthari, A., 2009. A framework for analysis design and operation of complex large scale sociotechnological systems. *International Journal for Decision Support Systems and Technologies,* 1(2), pp.52–68.

61. Taylor, B., 1971. The future development of corporate strategy. *Journal of Business Policy,* 2(2), pp.22–38.

62. The King v Chancellor [1722]1 Str. 557 93 (University of Cambridge), p.567.

63. Thompson, R., 2006. *Stakeholder analysis: winning support for your projects.* [online] Mindtools.com. Available at: https://www.mindtools.com/pages/art icle/newPPM_07.htm [Accessed 21 October 2019].

64. TopTenz, 2014. *Ten abandoned malls worth exploring.* [video] Available at: https ://www.youtube.com/watch?v=UvTMoy8mKKw [Accessed 14 October 2019].

65. Tuchman, B., 1985. *The march of folly: from Troy to Vietnam.* New York: Random House Trade.
66. Unknown, Flash flood early warning system (FFEWS), Chapter 9.
67. Watt, A., 2014. *Project management.* Victoria, BC: BCcampus.
68. Wheatley, M., 2006. *Leadership and the new science.* Kennett Square, PA: Soundview Executive Book Summaries.
69. Whelton, M. and Ballard, G., 2002. Wicked problems in project definition. *Proceedings of the 10th Annual Conference International Group for Lean Construction,* Brazil. Available at: http://www.leanconstruction.org/media/docs/WickedP roblemsinProjectDefinitionIGLC10.pdf [Accessed 25 June 2016].
70. Williams, B. and van't Hof, S., 2014. *Wicked solutions: a systems approach to complex problems, version 1.03.* 2nd ed. North Carolina: Lulu.com
71. Wood, H.L. and Ashton, P., 2010. *Modelling project complexity. In modelling project complexity.* Brighton, UK: University of Brighton, Association of Researchers in Construction Management, pp.1–3.
72. Youker, R., 1998. Defining the hierarchy of project objectives. In: *IPMA Conference.* [online] Available at: http://www.ipma-usa.org/articles/m_hiero bjs.pdf [Accessed 18 October 2019].

Additional readings

1. Cushman, M., Venters, W., Cornford, T. and Mitev, N., 2002. Understanding sustainability as knowledge practice. In: *Presented to British Academy of management conference: fast-tracking performance through partnerships,* London, UK.
2. Fryer, P., 2016. *What are complex adaptive systems? A brief description of complex adaptive systems and complexity theory.* Trojan Mice. [online] Available at: http://www.trojanmice.com/articles/complexadaptivesystems.htm and on http://web.mit.edu/esd.83/www/notebook/ComplexityKD.PDF [Accessed 20 January 2020].
3. Hoehne, O.M., 2010. Systems engineering in major capital projects. In: *2010 Rail Conference.* Vancouver, Canada, 2010-6-6 to 2010-6-9. Washington, DC: American Public Transportation Association, pp.1–10.
4. INCOSE Transportation Working Group, 2014. *Systems engineering in transportation projects, issue 7.0.* INCOSE. [online] Available at: http://www.incose.org/docs/default-source/TWG-Documents/incose-twg-case-study-li brary-7_0.pdf?sfvrsn=0 [Accessed 20 January 2020].
5. International Finance Corporation, (IFC), 2007. *Stakeholder engagement good practice handbook for companies doing business in emerging markets.* [ebook] [online] Available at: https://www.ifc.org.wps/wcm/connect/a6ed6140-b5ce-4e37-9f22-d9af5ee122c7/StakeholderEngagement1_Handbook_May15 _2007.pdf?MOD=AJPERES&CVID=jqeukAV [Accessed 21 October 2019].
6. Katz, D. and Kahn, R.L., 1966. *The social psychology of organizations.* New York, NY: Wiley, p.489. [Dept. Psychol., Survey Research Center, Univ. Michigan, Ann Arbor, MI].

7. Morris, Peter W.G., 2005. Managing the front-end: how project managers shape business strategy and manage project definition. In: *PMI 2005 Global Congress Proceedings*, Edinburgh, Scotland. [online] Available at http://www .indeco.co.uk/filestore/Morris-ManagingtheFront-End2005.pdf. Also available at https://www.pmi.org/learning/library/managing-front-end-project-busine ss-strategy-7500 [Accessed 20 February 2020].

Index